DNA

Ron Mackenna has worked as a political journalist on many of Scotland's top newspapers and is co-author, with Carlos Alba, of *Keep the Faith: the Story of Celtic's Historic Treble Winning Season 2000–2001*.

DNA

AND THE HUNT FOR
BRITAIN'S MOST EVIL KILLERS

RON MACKENNA

BLACK & WHITE PUBLISHING

First published 2003
by Black & White Publishing Ltd
99 Giles Street, Edinburgh EH6 6BZ

ISBN 1 902927 50 8

A CIP catalogue record for this book
is available from The British Library.

Printed and bound by Creative Print and Design

CONTENTS

For Debbie, Calum and Luca

Thanks to Professor Sir Alec Jeffreys, Martin Fairley of Strathclyde Police Forensic Science Unit, Strathclyde Police Press Office, Leicestershire Constabulary, The Forensic Science Service, Dr Peter Gill, Chief Superintendent David Baker, Dr James Weber, John Quinn, Dr Edward Blake, Johnny Dunne and the many people who helped me but asked to remain anonymous. Any mistakes are mine.

1

BANG TO RIGHTS

Almost twenty years have passed since Lynda Rosemarie Mann was buried in the pretty church graveyard at Narborough. Yet the gardener doesn't hesitate for a second when asked to point out where she lies.

'There's always a few people every year ask to see Lynda's grave,' he says, before taking me to it.

On the ground a brown, withered wreath still lies where it was placed on the day of her funeral. The headstone bears the inscription: 'We didn't have time to say goodbye but you're only a thought away.'

There is a childlike feel to the grave. White marble chips are spread across it, interspersed with bright blue translucent stones. The stones are the shape and colour of the fake jewellery favoured by young teenage girls the world over when they are experimenting with attracting boys. Their almost neon tones echo the garish covers of the teen magazines you see piled high in newsagents, with their photographs of boy bands and breezy promises of sure-fire love advice for even the most angst-ridden youngster.

Such was Lynda's world way back in 1983 when Boy George was camping it up the charts with 'Karma Chameleon', Elton John was singing 'I Guess That's Why They Call It the Blues' and Nik Kershaw was every schoolgirl's dream. Billowy parachute pants were in fashion and it had been a brilliant summer with long hot evenings for hanging out and gossiping. Her home village was a form of paradise for youngsters – small enough so that everybody knew everybody else yet close enough to the bustling metropolis of Leicester to ensure that the latest fashions and records were only a bus ride away.

Narborough was also quiet enough for parents to give their children the sort of freedom city kids of Lynda's age only dreamed about. There had never been any real crime. Like any village where people live in each other's pockets, familiarity suppressed it. And Narborough was linked to the neighbouring villages of Enderby and Littlethorpe by a network of beautiful footpaths that allowed youngsters to wander along them free from the ever-present dangers of traffic. It was a cosy and comfortable existence for a fifteen-year-old and one that Lynda had revelled in. She'd had a few boyfriends but nothing heavy. She was good at school but not so driven that it became a burden. She told her friends and her mum, Kath, and stepdad, Eddie, that she was going to be a linguist when she grew up but, right now, she was just enjoying life.

It is November 1983, the twenty-first to be precise, and Lynda has raced home, grabbed a quick tea with her stepfather and changed into her latest purchase – the cool donkey jacket that all the kids are wearing. Clothes, especially fashionable ones, cost money. Lynda knows that and, rather than nag her parents for it, she has created a little piece of independence for herself by doing some part-time babysitting. The money she earned from Mrs Walker earlier today will go towards paying for the donkey jacket.

Lynda's home is a little semi on The Coppice, a short walk from Narborough village centre, up near the hospital. Look down on it now and you'll see her leaving as she heads off to the home of her best friend, Karen Blackwell. A quickly shouted goodbye to Eddie and she's gone with the confidence that comes to young people on the cusp of adulthood. Karen's mum runs the Kay's catalogue that the donkey jacket came from. Tonight Lynda is going to hand over £1.50 as part payment for it. After that, she has decided to head off to Enderby to see another friend, Caroline, and pick up a record.

She is true to her word. Shortly before 7.30 p.m. – just before the music for Britain's most famous soap, *Coronation Street*, booms out – she is heading out the door and setting off along one of those little footpaths towards Enderby . . .

It is now February 22, 1984 – a bleak midwinter's day. The streets which squeeze around All Saints Church are crammed with activity. The houses are so tightly packed around the old village church that it seems to be gasping for breath in the enclosed space. Cars bump on to the pavement to leave just enough room for others to pass. Men, women and teenagers, dressed in black, mill around before moving across the road, through the gate and into the graveyard. Rolling gently downhill towards the trees, it provides an oasis of space and quiet. On either side, are little footpaths with swinging metal gates marking their entrances. Up at the top, near the unused area of the cemetery, the best known of all the local footpaths, the Black Pad, begins its journey.

As the vicar begins to intone those final words, police officers with video cameras are panning the faces of the mourners, looking for an expression of guilt or even a glance towards the Black Pad – but there is nothing. More than a hundred people stand around the grave. Of course, the white marble chips aren't there or the blue ones or even the gravestone which cost just short of £800. But Lynda Rosemarie Mann is. She is there all right, slowly being lowered into the ground as, all around, those who had known her and loved her broke their hearts.

It would be many years before anybody knew what really happened but we know now. On that night, the night of 21 November, as her friends were settling down to watch *Coronation Street* on the telly, a horrible cold reality has come crashing into Lynda's youthful world.

When she left the house a few minutes ago, she was walking briskly. Now she is running. Running away from the man who loomed up in front of her in the sickly glow of the streetlight and unzipped his trousers – running, though she doesn't realise it, into the darkness.

But Lynda is an extremely mature girl for her age and, even while the terror is rising in her throat, she gains control of herself. The man has followed her on to the footpath but she turns and faces him. As he takes hold of her and leads her towards the open field beside them, her mind is racing. 'Talk to him.'

'What are you doing?' Lynda asks. 'What are you doing it for?'

Then, although she didn't realise it at the time, she said four words that made her attacker freeze in his tracks. The four words, he would later admit, that would ensure that the last thing she ever saw was his contorted face.

She was controlled up until the very end. She said she would re-move her own clothes and told him not to touch her new jeans in case he damaged them. The zip jammed but she got them down. She even had a brief conversation with him as he forced himself into her, saying it hurt 'a bit'. But all the time those four words were haunting him.

9

* * *

Visit Lynda's grave today and it is impossible not to see the Black Pad footpath. She lies facing away from it. Look over the top of her gravestone and only a hundred or so feet away is the footpath where she met her lonely frightening death. It takes a moment to stride through the cemetery gates, turn right and begin to travel along it towards Carlton Hayes Mental Hospital where the path ends. That's exactly the same route a young hospital porter took on the frosty morning of 22 November 1983. Nowadays streetlights hang above the black asphalt of the path – erected in December of that year, at a cost of £5500, to allay local fears. Back then it was unlit and unkempt. The woods in the hospital grounds pushed in at the side, making its arrow-straight route appear to get narrower and narrower. Back then, you could walk – like the hospital porter had done – along the path right up to the hospital. Now, because of what happened to Lynda, the path stops abruptly and forces pedestrians to turn right on to the pavement for the final few hundred yards to the hospital.

At around 7.30 a.m. in a spot which now lies behind a wooden fence, the young porter stopped, having seen something in the gloom. It was a body – Linda's body – stiff in the morning frost. She was naked from the waist down. A smear of ruby red blood ran from her nose. Frightened and unsure if what he was seeing was real, he stopped the first car that came by. Together he and its occupant approached Lynda. Her donkey jacket was pulled up behind her head, its sleeves riding high on her arms as though she had been dragged by it. Her jeans, shoes and underwear lay nearby.

That little donkey jacket of Lynda's became kind of famous then. As did her maroon top her black socks and, of course, the figure hugging jeans and tights that were rolled up, like they'd just been pulled off and left lying beside her body when it was found on that morning of 22 November. The police did door-to-door searches – they quizzed neighbours and friends; they pleaded through the newspapers for anybody who had seen her on that dark November evening to come forward. It was all in vain.

For a while her name was on the lips of everybody in Narborough as the horror of a young schoolgirl's senseless murder gripped the community. But, as the weeks turned into months and nobody was caught, well, life went on as it always does. That publicity and the aftershocks are not the reasons perfect strangers turn up to visit her grave a few times a year. Nor do they account for the pleasant gardener being happy to break from his routine and respectfully lead you to her graveside. The reason is that Lynda and another young girl just like her were to be the first. The first people ever to have their murderers tracked down and caught by the use of a scientific tool called DNA fingerprinting. Their names have gone into the history books and are referenced and cross-referenced in academic journals across the world.

But that was all in the future. When Lynda died, the technique that caught her killer had not even been invented. Her horrible random death was destined to be yet another of those unsolved cases that the police doggedly pursue then gradually, through the total absence of anything remotely resembling a clue, are forced to let slip through their fingers. Such cases are never closed. Ever. Every year in police offices throughout the UK, senior detectives will take down the files on the day of the crime's anniversary, look through them, maybe spend some time considering whether anything fresh has happened and then, more often than not, replace them to wait for another year.

Nobody expects them to be solved and, until recently, almost none ever were. But the procedure and the strong assertion that the case is 'active' provide reassurance for the families who have to cope not only with the brutal loss of a loved one but also with the gnawing knowledge that the murderer is still out there. And over time they too come to appreciate that resources are finite – there are only so many officers and so much time before attention switches to the next big case.

And so it should have been for Lynda. Fading newspaper files recorded the moment when a family was ripped apart, when an innocent young girl was brutally slain and a sleepy English village gained a reputation as a dark place, forever associated with murder.

It took three months for Lynda's small body, just five foot two and weighing exactly eight stone, to make the journey from the mortuary in Leicester to the graveyard in Narborough. During that time, police and pathologists puzzled over the marks on her face and, more speci-fically, the bruising on her chest. Were these caused by her killer kneeling on her to hold her down or were they made in her last fight for life? Of the ligature marks around her neck there was no doubt – she had been strangled to death.

The delay caused great upset to her family but, in the scientific prodding and puzzling that went on during that period, something extremely important was done. Before her body was released for the funeral, samples of semen and a couple of locks of her hair were taken away and carefully preserved.

And so life did go on – as it always does. Except that parents living in Narborough and Enderby always warned their children about the footpaths and reminded them that Lynda Rosemarie Mann's murder had never been solved.

It is difficult, therefore, to imagine the feelings that went through Robin Ashworth's mind, more than three years later, as he found himself, one summer evening on the Black Pad footpath, desperately searching for his daughter, Dawn.

It was the summer of 1986, the evening of July the thirty-first, and the parallels between Dawn's sudden disappearance and Lynda's were startling. Dawn lived in Enderby and had gone to visit friends in Narborough. It was a reasonably short walk along Ten Pound Lane, a footpath that linked the two villages and ultimately ended up at Narborough Cemetery. Failing to find her friends, Dawn then apparently set off for home again.

She should have been home by 7 p.m. to attend a party with her family. By 9.30 p.m., her parents were frantic with worry and, at 9.40 p.m., they had called the police. It was just after that time that Robin Ashworth began his search of all the routes she might have taken, ending up on the Black Pad. Dawn wasn't on the Black Pad. Nobody, not the police, her family or friends, realised at the time but her body was lying in a clump of bushes on Ten Pound Lane. Nobody, not the police, her family or friends, realised at the time – nobody except the murderer, that is. Her father, Robin, had walked past the very spot in the same way that Eddie had walked past Lynda's body in a similar search three years earlier.

Did Dawn hear the little red Honda C70 scooter as it buzzed towards her when she walked into Ten Pound Lane? Did she hear the engine as it revved down the gearbox and then suddenly silenced at the spot where she had passed only seconds before? Did she hear him as he placed his helmet on top of the wing mirror and started hurrying up the path behind her? If she did, what could she do? It was daylight. It was summer. So what if someone had got off a motorcycle and started walking up the same path? It was a free country after all.

But she was walking quickly. So quickly that, when he passed her at a jog, he only had milliseconds to look at her and smile. So quickly that he couldn't get far enough ahead to turn and face her squarely. So quickly that he didn't have time to get his trousers fully open as he spun round and headed back towards her. So quickly that she didn't see the space beside him and walk past and, instead, she screamed and darted towards the gate beside her.

His hand was over her mouth, his frightened voice breathing a desperate instruction into her ear – 'Shut up!' He said 'Shut up!' again when she pleaded with him not to hurt her, when she told him she was a decent churchgoing girl and said 'Don't hurt me.' And, as he would later tell the police himself, she was 'petrified'. Calm, but petrified, she promised never to tell anyone if he would just leave – but this time he wouldn't even think twice about just leaving.

On the morning of Saturday 2 August, a sharp-eyed policeman noticed a finger protruding from a thorn bush in a field off Ten Pound Lane. Piles of weeds, grass and branches had been heaped on to the bush in an attempt to hide its grim contents. When they were gingerly removed, Dawn Ashworth was discovered lying on her left side in the foetal position with an arm stretched out in front of her. She was naked from the waist down, her pants dangling on one foot, her white shoes strangely still in place. Among the enormous number of injuries to the fifteen-year-old's body – some caused after death when her body was dragged to where it lay, others caused by the insects and animals which had come across her lying there in the intervening period – there were a couple which chilled detectives. It wasn't the damage caused by someone brutally having sex with her. It was the damage to her larynx that caused police officers to freeze as they immediately realised that the person who had carried out the attack on this fifteen-year-old child was probably the same maniac who had strangled Lynda Rosemarie Mann to death.

The death of a child brings out an extraordinary level of activity from any police force. Police officers are human beings. They have wives, daughters and sons at home. Murders are still rare. No matter how often an officer has to deal with the death of another human being in his daily life, the revulsion that is generated from the death of a child drives him or her as though it was the very first case they had ever dealt with. And so it had been in Lynda's case. Hundreds of officers had been drafted in, thousands of man hours expended and tens of thousands of pounds spent in an attempt to solve what finally appeared to be the random act of a chaotic mind.

Gradually the relatives and close friends were eliminated and with them went any of the fragments of a motive that are vital to try to pick up the trail of a killer. In mid 1984, when the inquiry was being wound down, the number of possible suspects stood at around thirty. It would reduce further to a list of eight. Eight men's names kept in a locked filing cabinet. Those whose details were typed out on that sheet of paper didn't know they were on it and the detectives, who occasionally scanned the list, knew they probably never would because there was not a real shred of evidence to indicate any one of them had done it. In short, nobody had been apprehended but it had not been for a lack of trying.

Imagine, therefore, the tremor of shock that went through Leicestershire Constabulary when the realisation broke over them that Lynda Mann's killer had probably, and it was just probably, struck again.

Of course, in a small community where police officers live among the people they serve, where journalists come and go and where, in times of crisis, rumours can sweep through the streets like wildfire, it didn't take long for the public to find out that they had a double killer living in their midst.

And, if anyone had any doubts, the crime reporter on the *Leicester Mercury* broke the news anyway in spectacular style. 'The sex killer who brutally murdered Dawn Ashworth almost certainly attacked and strangled Lynda Mann, another schoolgirl, whose body was found a few hundred yards away near Carlton Hayes Hospital less than three years ago,' his report screamed. 'Detectives hunting the killer, many of whom investigated Lynda's killing, today asked for maximum public help to catch "a very sick person" and said that a tiny scratch on a man's face could be a vital clue to the killer.'

The report claimed Dawn had put up a vigorous struggle to defend herself from her attacker though, in reality, the post-mortem report noted there was little sign of that. This was probably because of abject terror or the mistaken belief that, if she went along with what her attacker wanted, she would be spared.

It was not just the similar modus operandi that allowed the police to concede that the two girls had probably, just probably, died at the hands of the same killer. By analysing the semen found on both dead girls they reckoned they had found something that linked both murders. Admittedly, it was a pretty ropey forensic technique they were relying on but it was all they had to go on.

In both cases, a large amount of semen had been found in the pubic hairs of the girls – deposited, probably, when the murderer or murderers had suffered from premature ejaculation. It was a well-known medical fact that, by analysing semen, the blood group of the person who supplied the sample could be discovered. Not just semen but saliva, perspiration and other bodily fluids carry telltale markers of the person's blood group. What's less well known is that this does not apply to everybody. A small percentage of the population, one in five, are what is known as non-secreters. Their bodily fluids contain no trace of the markers that indicate blood type. In the '80s, it was every senior police officer's nightmare to discover that he was dealing with a non-secreter.

In the case of the two Enderby murders, police received good news and bad. The good news was that they were dealing with a secreter. The bad news was that, unfortunately, he was group A, a characteristic he had in common with twenty per cent of the population. However, the sperm count had been very high, indicating it had come from a youngish man. It wasn't much to go on but it was a start.

If the killer thought he was in for a relatively easy ride again, he was in for a shock. What followed was a storm of publicity. Local newspapers, horrified by the prospect of a double child murderer on the loose and irritated that the first murder had not been cleared up, went on the warpath.

One murder can pass relatively unnoticed – double murders never do. Narborough went nationwide. The national newspapers weighed in too. On the ground, police resources were poured into the villages. The number of bobbies on the beat was tripled, the murder squad swelled enormously, a giant sign 'murder here' went up at Ten Pound

Lane and then, overnight, the whole nation was suddenly involved.

Crimewatch UK, a prime-time programme dedicated to tackling unsolved crimes, had decided to go big on the Narborough murders. Overnight, television vans, catering and lighting trucks, presenters, technicians, editorial assistants and miles of thick black cable began winding their way around Dawn Ashworth's parents' house. Television crews also descended on Ten Pound Lane or Green Lane as it was known to the folk from Narborough. Millions of viewers across the United Kingdom settled down in their armchairs and watched spellbound as every single detail known to the police was beamed into their homes.

The net was being cast widely – possibly more widely than in Lynda Mann's murder. If the person responsible was an out-of-town killer, somebody perhaps who just visited the area occasionally, then he too would be pulled in through his family or friends or anybody who had reason to be suspicious about his behaviour. It wouldn't be the first time it had happened. The body of seven-year-old Susan Maxwell had been discovered in Leicestershire – dumped there by the van-driving monster, Robert Black, who had abducted her from her home many, many miles away.

It was a monumental effort, sending the intensity of a highly localised murder enquiry reverberating around a nation of fifty million people. Nobody doubted it was an absolutely vital step in the search for a psycho.

Actually, although nobody knew it just then, the girls' murderer was living just around the corner.

Crimewatch UK or not, the local population were electrified into action by the realisation that there could be a double murderer in their midst. Clues and sightings of Dawn's last walk came pouring in. Conversations with friends and neighbours were reported to the police. Seemingly innocuous statements amongst people who had known each other for years were plucked out of their settings and carried to the local constabulary. Amidst this blizzard of information – some helpful, most not – one thing began to make its presence known to the police amongst the mist that had descended on Dawn's last steps: a red step-through Honda motorcycle. It just kept cropping up in reports from people who gone past the end of Ten Pound Lane at around the same time that Dawn had died. Four separate eyewitnesses recalled it. Two reported seeing it parked there around 4.45 p.m. on the day of the murder. A third claimed it had still been there thirty minutes later – or at least a motorcycle with a red helmet hanging from the bars had been there. Someone else saw a man with a red helmet riding up and down the main road at the end of the lane on the days prior to the body being found.

Two police officers even reported seeing the man on a bike with a red helmet the day before Dawn's body had been discovered. Then there was the young man who had pushed his motorcycle up to a policeman on control duty at the murder scene and claimed to have actually seen Dawn on the evening she died. The motorcyclist actually gave his name and address. The conversation was noted meticulously and, within days, a detective had been sent around to interview him about his sighting. At that time, it was just another link in the evidence being gathered to pinpoint Dawn's final movements. At that time, all those other motorcycle sightings were just coming in and hadn't been correlated.

When the police added the young man's name to their mountain of suspicious information and started to look more closely at him, alarm bells started clanging loudly in the heads of the most senior officers. It wasn't just the fact that he worked at Carlton Hayes Hospital, the mental institution which loomed over the area where the girls' bodies had been found – although that was interesting. A great deal of effort had, in the past, gone into trying to calm local fears that one of the crazy patients had somehow found a way to sneak out and was on the rampage around the villages. In reality, nobody being treated there had stuck out as a likely candidate. In fact, there were no in-patients being treated for disorders of a sexual nature. And, anyway, it was just too pat, too Hammer House of Horror to be true.

During the first murder, employees had been looked at in the same way as all other members of the population. It was an employee, after all, who had discovered Lynda Rosemarie Mann's body that cold, frosted morning.

Yes, it was interesting that the mystery motorcyclist should spend a large part of his working days only yards from the two murder sites but that wasn't the half of it. As detectives went back up to the hospital to talk to other staff they made a startling discovery. They unearthed a nugget of information of the type that every murder squad detective hopes to come across. It was the sort of slip that paints a guilty party into a corner – a corner with bars across it.

This slip came from a friend of the motorcyclist. He told officers that, the night after Dawn had gone missing and the day before she had been found, the motorcyclist had visited him at home and told him something very interesting. He had said that Dawn had been discovered 'in a hedge near a gate by the M1 bridge' which, as every local knew, just about perfectly described Ten Pound Lane and the spot where Dawn's body had been found. Crucially the friend's father had overheard this conversation and wondered out loud to the motorcyclist why it hadn't been on the telly. 'Someone told me,' the motorcyclist added.

Then someone else told police that the motorcyclist had met him on the day Dawn's body was discovered and he had announced, 'She's dead.' This was some hours before the discovery had been made public.

Five a.m. door knocks are rarely benign. Unless it's a workaholic postman, it's safe to assume it's probably bad news. When the police arrived at the motorcyclist's door at five o'clock, they weren't there for routine questioning.

As four detectives brusquely moved past his startled mother, a chain of events was thrown into sequence that would bring the full majesty of the law, with all it's grinding and impersonal machinery, crashing down on the young man's head.

The date was now Friday 8 August – just over a week after Dawn had gone missing. This time there was to be no repeat of the months of agony and pain that had followed Lynda Rosemarie Mann's death. This time the police had been able to eliminate the family from the suspect list almost immediately. Lynda's stepfather, Eddie, had undergone the shame and misery of being blood-tested as part of the inquiry into her murder. This time they were sure they had their man.

As the motorcyclist was woken from his bed and stumbled into the light he heard the words that countless other police suspects have heard the length and breadth of Britain. Unlike many others he was totally unprepared for them.

'I'm arresting you on suspicion of being concerned in the death of

Dawn Ashworth. I must tell you, you do not have to say anything unless you wish to do so but anything you say may be given in evidence. Do you understand that?' Understand them he most certainly did. But listen to exactly what the officers were saying? No.

At roughly the same time that he should have been starting work, the man – young man, boy, really, for he was only seventeen – was sitting in a police interview room in nearby Wigston Police Station. His name was Richard Buckland and he was frightened. Frightened enough to ignore the part about not saying anything. He started talking and barely stopped during the rest of the day.

Of course, on that Friday, he wasn't charged with anything. British law is very peculiar about the rights and powers of police officers when dealing with suspects. Once a person is charged, he or she becomes strictly off limits to the investigating authorities. And, apart from that, the initial evidence was only circumstantial.

The interviews were, of course, taped. And alone, without his parents, a series of police officers began the age-old task of coaxing the incriminating details – the checkable facts that would amount to a confession – from him.

It didn't really take that long for a strong picture to come tumbling out. Where was he on the afternoon of Dawn Ashworth's death? At around 4.30 p.m., he had been on his motorcycle taking it for a test run along the very road that Ten Pound Lane began from. Had he seen Dawn? Yes. Had he stopped? No. Well, yes. Just to look at oil that was leaking from the bike's engine. Why did he tell his friend that her body had been found? He didn't tell the friend. The friend told him. Had he spoken to Dawn? No. He went straight home. Yes. He had had a brief conversation with her, walked halfway up the lane with her, then got on his bike and went straight home. No, that hadn't been that day. It had been the day before. And so it went on. Backwards and forwards, partial confession, retraction, straight answer, then confusion.

During the interview, he alluded to other extremely minor, but disturbing, incidents involving other girls. They were checked out and confirmed. A picture was beginning to emerge of a young man who was sexually immature, as most boys his age are, but who had had sexual encounters with girls who were younger than he was. In the course of the day, he admitted that he had followed girls he 'fancied' in the village. He also seemed to have an extremely low opinion of females, admitting to calling them 'slags and whores' on occasion. Things were slotting into place.

Fourteen hours after the interviews had first begun, the police had heard varying stages of a confession. Pictures of Dawn's last minutes were being pieced together by the officers. Snapshots of a young girl screaming. A hand going up her skirt. Then hands up her blouse. The young man stifling her cries with his hands, pressing hard on her mouth, her nose, snuffing out those cries. Then hiding her. Unfortunately they also heard him say that he hadn't had to pick her up to hide the body, even though everybody for miles around knew she had been dragged into the bushes and covered. Then he said, 'I'm trying to tell you the truth! I'm trying to prove to you that it's not me that done it. I don't even know where she was hid. I said that to that officer.'

It was exhausting for everybody concerned. Then, late in the evening, after he had been read his rights again, Buckland came out with his most coherent picture of what had happened. The question (see Joseph Wambaugh, *The Blooding* (New York: Bantam Books, 1989) p. 175) had been: 'What made you do what you did?' 'What? Hit her?' he replied. 'Just 'cause I liked her at the time. I wanted someone to have sex with and I didn't think she would let me so I tried it on.' All right so far. 'Then she started panicking so I thought, "If I leave her, she'll tell her mum and dad and I'll be in trouble." So I did something about it. She started screaming so I put me hand over her mouth. I took her pants off and had sex with her and buried her and that's all I remember doing. I walked straight back down the lane.' Bingo. The local newspaper trumpeted the headline 'Dawn: Local youth held'. The whole village knew who had been arrested and why.

He appeared in court on the Monday morning in yet another of those legal practices that appear curious to those who don't make their living from the law. For locals, awaiting details of what had actually happened, there were none. The boy stood in the dock for a matter of minutes, confirmed his name and a few other points of minutiae and then was remanded into police custody. The trial – his trial – would be scheduled for some time in the coming months.

But there was a problem – a major problem. And it wasn't the alibi, offered by his mother, that he'd been sitting at home, watching *Heidi* on television, when the murder of Dawn Ashworth was supposed to have taken place. Juries all over the world tend to take alibis from wives, mothers and other assorted members of the accused's family with a pinch of salt. Blood is thicker than water, they always think, and, hey, they'd probably do the same thing for their own son.

No, the problem was Lynda Rosemarie Mann. Nobody in their right mind doubted the same person had carried out both murders. Copycat? Nah. That sort of stuff was for the detective novels. The modus operandi in both killings had been strikingly similar and the method of death chillingly so. Yet young Buckland had steadfastly refused to take any blame whatsoever for the first killing. True it had been three years ago but he was a powerful lad with strong sexual urges. There was also a pattern emerging of his inability to deal with females in a form that would be considered decent by any civilised society.

As the police had got to work, other incidents had emerged. In themselves, they were minor but enough to convince them that here was a young man who had been going off the rails for some considerable time.

However, the lack of anything to link him with both slayings was gnawing away at everybody. Conviction for one murder would take him off the streets for a very long time but there was the question of police professionalism, not to mention the closure that was long overdue for Lynda Rosemarie Mann's parents.

The damn blood tests hadn't worked either. It was always a bit of a long shot but Buckland's blood test, the one he'd asked for, hadn't tied him to the two killings. But science could still help. One afternoon, shortly after Buckland had been remanded in custody, the telephone rang in a science laboratory in the bowels of Leicester University, only a few miles from the police station where the interview had taken place. The man who picked it up sat in a narrow office crammed with books along one wall and with a simple desk and computer along another. Outside, through the thin partition, a chemistry lab was in full swing. Glass beakers bubbled, machines spun and students and assistants in white lab coats moved briskly from bench to bench. The reason for all the activity was a startling discovery that had recently been made by the man who answered the telephone. It had transformed the dry and dusty field in which he studied from a purely academic pursuit and catapulted him and his colleagues into the racy world of courts and lawyers. His discovery had nothing to do with police work, yet, but that was all about to change.

The man's name was Alec Jeffreys and, as he held the telephone receiver to his ear, a voice at the other end introduced himself as a police officer from Leicestershire Constabulary. There was a tricky double murder, the officer continued, and a man in custody. Would it be possible for Dr Jeffreys to use his new technique to ascertain whether semen samples taken from two separate crime scenes had come from the same person and even, possibly, identify that person from those samples.

The scientist was used to strange requests. His life had recently been turned upside down by what he had stumbled across. He had been in the newspapers – the *Readers Digest* had even done a big article on him. Ordinary members of the public routinely tried to buttonhole him to get his help. But this was taking his technique into a wholly new area. He was already snowed under with work. In fact, 'under siege' was how he would later describe it. Why on earth take on something totally different? Something that his instincts said would probably not have a cat's chance in hell of working.

He paused and, on that pause, the lives of countless hundreds of people hung in the balance. The future of young Buckland, for it was also about him, depended on Alec Jeffreys' decision too. Then Dr Jeffreys replied, 'Yes, we'll try. That's all we can do.' And the world changed.

Although he little knew it, the young motorcyclist, sitting in a nearby police cell at that very moment, was to take a strange place in history as a result of that conversation. But there would be many more strange outcomes before that happened.

2

GOD'S FINGERPRINTS

Alec Jeffreys leans across the table, picks some tobacco out of his Golden Virginia tin and makes himself a roll up. Relaxing in his seat with a cigarette between his lips and his scuffed shoes crossed in front of him, he has the air of an impoverished student despite his fifty-two years. 'That's it there,' he says, suddenly pointing at a black and white picture on the wall of his office. 'That's the actual photograph and, yes, it did change my life. Unquestionably.'

The date of this event was 15 September 1984. The time was somewhere around 8.30 a.m. Such is Alec Jeffreys' recall that he can reel off exactly what he did in the minutes that ticked down to what he calls his 'Eureka' moment. Surprising, perhaps, considering he had absolutely no idea what he was about to discover. 'I had cereal and toast, then a cup of tea in the house – my wife doesn't have anything. I drove into the university and came into the lab here. I thought, "I'll look and see if this new probe we're working on has shown anything." The x-ray film had been developing in the deep freeze over the weekend. So I took the cassette into the dark room, warmed it up and put the film in the fixative for a few minutes. At that point, you can have a look. I pulled it out and holy shit! I just thought, "Oh boy! We're on to something really big, something really unexpected here." It was that obvious. In those five minutes, my life totally changed.'

The photograph, pinned to the wall behind him, explains why. Written across the top in large uneven ballpoint letters are the words 'THE WORLD'S FIRST DNA FINGERPRINT'.

He may be too modest to come right out with it but, in those five minutes, Alec Jeffreys, or Professor Sir Alec Jeffreys as he is known now, also changed the world. Within months, as news of it flashed around the globe, his discovery would take him out of his chemistry lab – with its test tubes and whirling separating machines – and into

23

the courts, the heart of government and on to the front pages of newspapers. It would also eventually earn him the knighthood he wishes he had had 'the courage to turn down', make him a freeman of the City of Leicester and land him so many awards that he jokes he now has 'probably more letters after his name than anyone else in Britain'.

That morning, however, the first person he told was his colleague, Vicky Wilson, who had worked side by side with him on what was meant to be a project to find ways of mapping the human gene in more detail. 'It was very exciting. We ran back into the lab. We could see all sorts of applications. Things were running through my brain in an incoherent fashion. We drew up a sort of shopping list.'

In the evening, as he sat at home with his wife, Sue, babbling excitedly about what had happened in the lab, he outlined a list of possible applications, including tracing the parenthood of wild animals or proving the pedigree of dogs. They were all significant but hardly earth moving.

As he recalls, it was Sue who saw the bigger picture. 'She said, "Well, actually, there's another area you have forgotten about." I said, "Okay, what is it?" and she replied, "Immigration disputes." I thought, "Shit! This is no longer just science. This is public policy. Politics."'

Each human chromosome is one long twisting DNA molecule with chemical letters repeating themselves over and over again, ad nauseam, down its length, millions of times. By the late 1970s, the glorious double helix model of human DNA, discovered by James Watson and Francis Crick, was instantly recognisable to huge sections of the population. It was a symbol of scientific development – proof that the human race was on the brink of unlocking the blueprint of its own creation. Unfortunately, it was also an almost total enigma.

Scientists could point to this area or that and say they believed it contained such and such a piece of information. But, by and large, the human chromosome was a dark continent viewed as if from the bridge of a pitching ship, miles out at sea. Explorers were already leaving the ship and sailing towards the mystery land, in the hope of uncovering the treasures contained within, but, like all great ventures, everybody knew it would take decades before all the questions were answered.

The prizes were Eldorados, golden cities containing unimaginable riches for the human race. Speculation ran wild that, when the human genome was unlocked, it would provide the ability to tinker with fundamental aspects of human life. Maybe the gene concerned with the secret of longevity could be reprogrammed to halt decay and herald an era of eternal youth. If a gene could be found to show a person had a predisposition to develop cancer, it could be turned off like a light switch – as, perhaps, could all those other rogue genes which were suspected of unleashing the damaging illnesses and genetic defects which blight the human race. They were heady days but, even if reality was to prove a bit more sobering, the importance of Watson and Crick's discovery could never have been underestimated. However, back then, the fundamental problem was that, when the gene maps of individual human beings were examined for differences, they turned out to appear depressingly similar.

In 1975, the year he graduated with a doctorate in biochemistry, the young Alec Jeffreys decided this crowded, yet exciting, arena was where his future career lay. Jeffreys, the son of an engineer and a product of a resolutely middle-class English family, had always shown promise. Few people who graduate from Oxford with a first class honours degree can be described in any other terms. Armed with his doctorate, he headed to Amsterdam to work on a research project whose aim was to try to clone what is known as a single-copy gene. The project failed to achieve this but, along the way, a sure-fire method of identifying single-copy genes was discovered. It was a modestly rewarding achievement and, with his career established, Alec Jeffreys applied for a job in the Biochemistry Department of the University of Leicester.

He got it and, on his return to England in 1977, he embarked on a new field of research. The focus of his attention was to be the evolution of genes and the variation in DNA patterns. His work, for the next seven years or so, was to consist mainly of mapping the little inlets and bays of human DNA. Important, certainly, but, at the time, it was not thought likely to stand the world on its head.

In 1980, an academic paper was published reporting a strange phenomenon in the human chromosome. There appeared to be randomly repeated sections – or stuttered sections, as they came to be known – in the DNA code. It looked as though, at last, someone had found a let-up in what was beginning to look like the endlessly boring terrain of the human genome.

These mysterious but eye-catching new sections were labelled as 'hypervariable', which is the scientist's way of describing something that is extremely irregular or unpredictable. To explain their significance, it is important to appreciate how regular DNA code had been thought to be until this point.

You don't need to have spent a lifetime studying genetics to appreciate the apparently infinite variation in the human race. To the naked eye, no two people are ever exactly the same (except, perhaps, identical twins). The differences are endless and magnificent. It's not just hair type, eye colour, skin pigmentation, height or nose lengths. Behaviourally, people are all unique and, despite millennia of civilisation, almost impossible to sort into easy classifications.

Given the obvious variety in the human race, who wouldn't assume that this veritable explosion of diversity in the appearance of humans would also be reflected in our DNA code? In fact, in the early 1980s, if you took a human being, sampled his or her blood and then evaluated their DNA code, what you would find would be a pattern that looked far from unique. Everybody's DNA looked the same and we were all represented by just four chemical letters, appearing over and over again, apparently totally at random. There seemed to be nothing more and nothing less – just these bewildering and not very interesting series of letters.

So, when stuttered sections were discovered, it was like discovering a chink in nature's cloaking device. Human DNA moved from black and white to a world where there were outbreaks of primary colours. The repeated sections injected life and mystery into the human genome. It appeared as though suddenly one chemical letter would become dominant, quietly run riot and then the four-letter randomness would return. An example would be, if an ordinary section of the sequence read 'The Quick Brown Fox', a stuttered section would appear as 'The QQQQQQQQQQQQQQQQQuick Brown Fooooooooox'. The world of science was fascinated.

It didn't take long for the scientific community to realise that, if someone could work out where these crazy sections could be found, then they could be used as route markers to other pieces of DNA. However, stumbling across them was one thing, predicting where they'd turn up on the enormously long DNA highway was to prove almost impossible. Eventually, as is the nature of such matters, people moved on to other things.

In 1984, Dr Alec Jeffreys was deep into his work on the evolution of genes when a piece of vacuum-packed meat arrived in his office. It had been cut from the body of a grey seal on the artic shelf. It was then transferred to the British Antarctic Expedition's headquarters in Cambridgeshire and, from there, on to Dr Jeffreys' laboratory at Leicester. It was to prove a historic journey.

The grey seal was selected for a reason. They have an unusual characteristic that humans lack. It is the ability to store large amounts of their oxygen in their blood. That's why a lump of blubber can transform itself into a graceful sub-aquatic ballet dancer. Seals are able to hold their breath for a long time because of the huge levels of myoglobin and haemoglobin coursing around their bodies. These extra high levels allow them to carry much more oxygen in their muscles and blood than human beings can so that, when they are deep under water, they can use that oxygen to keep their hearts, brains and muscles functioning.

However, Jeffreys and his team weren't trying to create anything as mundane as the man from Atlantis. They were still heavily involved in that esoteric project to try to discover the steps involved in human evolution. Anthropologists had long speculated that, at one time, the genes responsible for the production of myoglobin and haemoglobin had been the same. They believed that, millions of years ago, as human beings went through some long lost evolutionary change, these genes had split. The project was designed to take some of the abundant samples of these genes from the seal and identify their characteristics. Then they could be used to hunt down the same genes in human beings and this would allow them to try to establish whether this split had taken place. It was to lead, accidentally, to sensational results.

As he lights another roll-up, a cloud of concentration looms over Dr Jeffreys' face. He recalls, 'We used the seal gene to get the human gene. Inside the human gene, what we saw was a bit of DNA with a chemical sequence repeated over and over again.'

It was a result. They had found the stuttered DNA again. What's more, there was also a strong clue that these stuttered regions did, in fact, appear at recognisable points within the human DNA. Even more interestingly, there was the slim possibility that they might, for some reason, vary for every person and organism tested.

Intrigued, Jeffreys designed a probe – a sort of Mars landing craft for the human genome. The hope was that it would latch on to the stuttered areas and allow them to be closely examined and even mapped. Around 7 September, he prepared another experiment to try to verify the results he had achieved with the seal meat. This time his sample material was much wider. It was a virtual cooking pot of genetic material with animal and human DNA tossed in together to give as wide a cross section of material as he could come up with.

'We kind of hoped the probe would detect lots of these stuttered regions at the same time,' Jeffreys recalls. 'The probe is just a bit of radioactive DNA that does a chemical process called a Crick-Watson base pairing.'

On the Friday evening of 12 September, he turned the lights off in the lab and headed home, leaving the experiment to work away over the weekend. It was to be his last two days of normality with his family for some years.

Many years later, Alec Jeffreys is still working from the same little office in the same university building. To find him, turn up the security desk of the Adrian Building in Leicester University. The security guards will call his secretary, Nancy, and she'll take you the twenty feet round the corner and through the big wooden double doors that lead to the chemistry lab.

It looks just like a chemistry lab should. The walls are lined with glass receptacles of different shapes, various pieces of heavy scientific equipment are spread around the room and everywhere people are moving around in white lab coats. Near the middle, just across from the door, is a glorified cubicle with a computer at one end and set of packed bookshelves along the wall. It's in this office that I'm sitting as Alec Jeffreys talks about the crazy period in his life that followed that Friday in September of 1984.

Pointing once again at the photograph on the wall with the slightly skewed, blocky grey and black pattern, he is transported back to the following Monday morning. 'That's the real first one,' he says. 'I pulled it out the developer, put the light on and thought, "Holy shit!" It was awful, really crap, but you could see the principle so clearly. You could pick out he patterns of each individual's DNA in the photograph. They were all different. It was an extraordinary moment. We had some unrelated people in it and I could see the different patterns for them. Then we had a family group, mother, father and child, and I could see how the pattern was being inherited.'

What Jeffreys had stumbled upon was the barcode of life. It was crystal clear from the photograph that, instead of there being the same DNA sequence for everything he had tested, each was different and unique. Not just a little bit different but wildly, beautifully different – even to the naked eye.

'This was a rare moment in science because science usually proceeds step by painful step and things emerge slowly over time. This was a Eureka moment. I thought, "Oh, boy! We're on to something completely unexpected." In five minutes my life had totally changed.'

By the afternoon of that day, Jeffreys and his staff were taking pinpricks of blood from their fingers, smearing them on to glass and pieces of laboratory tissue and seeing if they could produce their own unique DNA profiles. And they could.

They had the answer but they didn't quite have the question. Jeffreys could show how every living thing was different but he wasn't quite sure what it could be used for. It would take almost a year and an unsolved murder case to come up with the killer application.

'It was basically a prime example of science coming up with an answer to a question that had not been asked,' remembers Jeffreys. 'We were all running about trying this new thing and seeing if it could be replicated.'

The magic of DNA fingerprinting is that it provides an apparently foolproof way of identifying every living thing's unique genetic make-up. A bank account number is a good analogy. The results of Jeffreys' DNA test assigned the equivalent of a bank account number to the person tested. That number, or code, is unique to that person and can never vary. But first they had to give it a name.

'The original slide was basically crap,' he says. 'The quality of the print wasn't particularly good and it wasn't as clear as we would have liked it to be. However, within a relatively short time, we had refined it so it gave much better pictures, which were much easier to read. It became a real biological product.

'We hadn't really thought about terminology but I was giving a talk over in Oxford and, at the end of the talk, I spent a couple of minutes showing these strange patterns. There was a good friend of mine there by the name of Nick Proudfoot. He came up and said "That was really interesting but actually they're a bit like fingerprints aren't they?" I thought, "That'll do." I have to say that, with the wisdom of hindsight, calling them DNA fingerprints was the smart thing to do. Had we called them "idiosyncratic southern block hyd-ridisation profiles", it would have killed it dead. It got the message across very quickly. We have had a lot of flak from forensic scientists, especially the finger-printers, who reckoned we were nicking their term. It has become corrupted and vague. That's why they don't like it.'

Jeffreys' discovery is startling when you consider it occurred in the era of privately funded laboratories with teams of scientists chipping away at tiny fractions of the known world. Genuine scientific break-throughs are few and far between. Research papers are published, more often than not, with screeds of names attached to them and filed with the shorthand 'et al.'. Et al., meaning 'and all the rest of the poor buggers who pitched in to come up with the result but whose names we can't be bothered to list because it will take up too much space'. The Latin phrase will be etched on the gravestone of modern science. It signifies that, by and large, the frontier spirit, which characterised science up until the early part of the last century, has disappeared.

So, when young scientists, begin their careers, they do so in the knowledge that the days of the instant world-changing breakthrough are largely gone. Their memory consigned to encyclopaedia references on people like the vet, John Boyd Dunlop, who invented the pneumatic tyre in his spare time because he was cheesed off with the crashing and banging every time he travelled in something with wheels. Or the undertaker, Almon B Strowger, who designed the automatic telephone exchange because he realised a business rival was bribing the local telephonist. Or, even more spectacularly, the two concert musicians,

Leopold Mannes and Leo Godowsky, who bought themselves a pile of science books and invented colour photography in their hotel bedroom.

Today, by and large, science has been handed over to the armies of professionals. It is now a strictly controlled and extremely slow moving profession. Laboratories are staffed with researchers trying to make tiny little discoveries which, if they're lucky, will advance the sum knowledge of the world by a microscopic amount. To the outsider, it looks very much like dancing on the head of a pin.

Like his peers, Jeffreys didn't work alone. His colleague, Vicky Wilson, for example, was extremely closely involved and he had his sponsors, the Lister Institute of Preventative Medicine, to consider every step of the way.

Their reaction to his discovery was as excited as that of everybody else. It was decided to patent the technique. For the humble scientist, the patenting process alone causes all sorts of problems – not least the imperative to keep quiet about it until the legal shackles had been put in place. Lawyers and technical experts were brought in to pore over the details of what Jeffreys had uncovered and make sure that it couldn't be copied or, worse, slightly altered to produce the same results.

'The patenting was painful because academics work in an atmosphere of academic freedom,' he recalls. 'We work by running around talking to each other. And then suddenly the patent agents and the funders were, quite rightly, saying we had to be careful about everything – not spread about what we had stumbled upon.'

To the casual observer, Jeffreys' Leicester lab was transformed into a hive of activity as high-powered meetings took place, outsiders began to turn up in significant numbers and all the time in the background Jeffreys and his team secretly worked to refine the quality of their DNA photographs.

By early 1985, the patents were finalised and were ready to be submitted. Meanwhile Jeffreys, Vicky Wilson and S L Thein completed the research paper, which was to be delivered to the world's most prestigious scientific journal, *Nature*. (See A J Jeffreys, V Wilson and S L Thein, 'Hypervariable "minisatellite" regions in human DNA', *Nature*, 314 (6006), 1985.) 'Hypervariable "minisatellite" regions in human DNA' may not have been the catchiest title dreamt up for an article that year

31

but it could well have been the most memorable.

Even on the brink of publication, Alec Jeffreys was far from convinced that his academic colleagues would react to the discovery with the same enthusiasm that his wife had all those months ago. 'To be truthful, my feeling was this may not go anywhere – people might not be interested,' he says. 'And, even if they were interested, it could take ten years to get this into the mainstream. We simply weren't familiar with the field. We didn't know what applications there could be in this.' But he needn't have worried. When the paper was published, it exploded on to the academic horizon like a starburst bombshell.

While all this scientific excitement was taking place, a world away a fifteen-year-old schoolboy was unwittingly about to play his part in the story of DNA fingerprinting. Andrew Sarbah was a normal lad who was unlucky enough to fall foul of that most prickly of British obsessions – immigration. Young Andrew had lived in London with his mother and would probably have continued to do so quite happily had it not been decided to send him to his father in Ghana for a long holiday. That holiday stretched into years and, when Andrew flew back into Heathrow to rejoin his mother, he had two passports – his original British one and a more up-to-date Ghanian version – it was the beginning of a nightmare of Kafkaesque proportions.

Instead of leaving the airport to meet his waiting relatives, the youngster found himself being ushered into a room by immigration officials. They spread his Ghanian passport before him and said it was a fake. Worse, they said there were serious doubts about his British passport and declared he was an illegal immigrant. What seemed at first to his family to be a case of over zealousness on the part of the Home Office rapidly degenerated into one of these dark little tragedies that is played out on a daily basis in airports the length and breadth of the UK.

Lawyers were brought in and, full of high hopes, Andrew and his mother separately gave blood samples to prove that they were telling the truth about their relationship. The blood was subjected to the most sophisticated battery of tests available in the United Kingdom in the late 1980s. In all, sixteen different genetic characteristics were evaluated from each sample of blood. The results, when they arrived weeks later, proved, without a shadow of doubt, that the two were, in fact, related.

The family gathered themselves for what they assumed would be the end of an extremely unpleasant matter. Unfortunately, it wasn't. The tests proved they were related but they could not determine exactly what relationship there was. The Home Office concluded that Andrew Sarbah, far from being the son of a UK resident, was, in fact, her nephew. And, of course, nephews have no rights of residence.

And so the affair would have ended. It attracted no publicity. Why should it? There was next to nothing newsworthy about it at all. The Home Office was turning back people claiming to be children of British citizens on a fairly regular basis, along with wives, husbands and Uncle Tom Cobbley and all. Nobody doubted that, amongst the huge tide of chancers looking for a better life, there might be the odd genuine case but the system was good and it certainly wasn't something that happened often – if at all.

It seemed a lost cause. Andrew's family had no access to expensive lawyers or teams of advisers to fight on their behalf. Instead, they had put their future in the hands of a charitable organization which, even today, survives on a turnover of just over half a million pounds and with a staff of just fourteen. Hammersmith and Fulham Community Law Centre stated its aims were 'the relief of poverty, suffering and distress and the advancement of education'. These were lofty ideals but they were unlikely to cut the mustard with the mandarins of the Home Office.

However, when just about everyone else on the planet would have given up any hope of reuniting Andrew with his mother, they did not. In what was to turn out to be a stroke of genius, they took a long shot on the boy's behalf. One of the centre's staff came into work one day talking about a tiny article in *The Guardian* newspaper that she'd read on the bus. It was about a scientific breakthrough that could seemingly prove parentage. Sheona York, who was dealing with the case, decided there was nothing to lose by ringing up Leicester University and trying to speak to the scientist mentioned in the article. She got through and, even today, Alec Jeffreys clearly recalls listening to her running through the whole Andrew Sarbah story. She said, 'You've got this new technique. Why don't you try it out on a real family?' He was moved by her conviction that a genuine wrong was happening. Taking one of those split-second decisions that were to play such a crucial role in his future, he told her, 'Okay, we'll give it a shot.' It had never been tried before but proving parentage was exactly the sort of thing Jeffreys' new test was supposed to do. It should have been straightforward.

By then, it was well known that everybody inherits their DNA pattern from their parents. Half of the bands in a person's DNA fingerprint comes from their father and the other half comes from their mother. To establish the parentage of a child, the technique is to take the mother's sample, compare the pattern to the child's and remove all the bands that match. The pattern that is left should be exactly the same as the father's. But, in this case, there was a problem – a major problem. Although blood samples were available for Andrew's mother and for Andrew, there was no sample available for his father. Jeffreys and his team racked their brains for a while and then came up with a very neat solution. They would take blood samples from Andrew, his mother and from her three other children. Andrew's mother's genetic coding was removed from the pattern created by her three children – or rather the three children who were without any doubt her children. What was left was a set of grey shaded bars that were identical for all three. That showed they all had the same father. Mrs Sarbah's pattern was then removed from Andrew's sample and his remaining pattern was overlaid against the father's pattern than had been obtained from the three other children. It was a perfect match. 'That was astonishing,' says Jeffreys who was as amazed at the success of his technique as anyone else.

The next problem was explaining to British government officials that they should take notice of a scientific technique they'd never heard of and which had been carried out by a scientist they'd never heard of. A preliminary hearing took place. It didn't go well. In fact, it ordered Andrew's deportation. 'We were astonished,' recalls Sheona York, now a solicitor. 'Their view was that this was some ridiculous scientific nonsense. We appealed and Alec Jeffreys volunteered to come down and give evidence. We had statistics to show that there was more chance of the Andrew being who he said he was than there were grains of sand in the whole world. Really. The Home Office brought in their own statistician and I remember him and Dr Jeffreys looking daggers at each other outside the courtroom. But the tribunal chairman recognised it was a revolutionary technique.'

'The Home Office hadn't got a clue what DNA fingerprinting was,' Jeffreys remembers. 'I had to explain what it was all about. The bottom line was they dropped the case against the boy. What they didn't want to do was make a legal ruling on the basis of DNA fingerprinting. They were worried about some sort of quasi-legal precedence.'

Andrew Sarbah had just earned himself a footnote in history as the first person whose life had been changed as a result of DNA fingerprinting. That detail paled into insignificance compared to the realisation that he wasn't going to be forcibly separated from his mother and family.

Looking back, Sheona York admits that history was made that day. But it didn't seem like that for the next couple of years. 'We attracted a certain amount of odium from people in the profession who believed that the Home Office would insist on the tests for all future cases and that would cause a great deal of embarrassment for some people. And it has in a few cases where women have been forced to concede that a child is not their own, thereby, bringing great embarrassment to their families and causing all sorts of turmoil and, sometimes, when a child has been brought up in a family from birth, splitting it. But you just fight the case you are dealing with at the time – not all the ones to come.'

DNA testing has also, undoubtedly, paved the way to a new life for thousands of immigrants who would otherwise have been turned away. All, perhaps, because of a newspaper story read on a bus. Does Sheona York still wonder at the turn of circumstances that followed her phone call? 'To be honest, I'm more amazed that Alec Jeffreys did the test, that he did it for nothing – even though we offered to pay – and that he came down to the hearing in London when he did not have to. He's a smashing bloke, I'm very happy to have met him and I was very, very impressed by him.'

Alec Jeffreys has warm memories of the case too. Particularly of the moment when Andrew's mother was told her son would not be deported. 'Of all the things that have happened in the whole story of DNA fingerprinting, that was the moment for me,' says Jeffreys. 'You could see the enormous sense of relief in Mrs Sarbah's eyes when she was told. That was magic. Here was science that had changed someone's life for good. I was actually in the lawyer's office when she was told the news that the nightmare was all over. It was a wonderful, wonderful moment. She had been fighting the case for years – it had affected her health – but, at that moment, all the trouble just disappeared from her.'

Alec Jeffreys' name appeared in *Nature* for a second time in a year. This time, he penned an article detailing the Sarbah case and illustrating the new and powerful use for DNA fingerprinting. The language and technical terms used in *Nature* are designed to resonate with its largely scientific readership. Journalists pore over the articles to try to winkle out the ones they can spin into human-interest stories. It is surprising how often a couple of phone calls to the authors of seemingly impenetrable research papers can shine a light on to the densest scientific terms. And, because of that article in *Nature*, the phone in Alec Jeffreys' office started ringing as interest surged in what was the first practical application for a new scientific technique that had only been revealed to the world a few months earlier.

The result of that growing interest was that, on 31 October 1985, *The Guardian* ran a piece entitled 'Son rejoins mother as genetic test ends immigration dispute Ghanian boy allowed to join family in Britain'. The newspaper reported that the 'decision could prove to be a landmark. The Home Office is considering using the test to determine paternity in other immigration disputes and the police are reported to be interested in using its potential for identifying criminals.' And *The Times* followed the story up the following day, saying 'proof that the boy was the son of Mrs Sarbah came from Dr Alec Jeffreys and his colleagues at Leicester University.' The cat was well and truly out of the bag and 'The next day there was a complete avalanche of requests,' Jeffreys says. 'We hadn't realised just how many people were trapped in these kind of situations and disputes. We were the only lab in the world that could do this test. It just got out of control. I was out in the garden one Sunday when people came walking through the back gate. It was a lawyer and an immigrant family from London who had driven all the way up to Leicester on the off chance. They said, "Will you take blood?" I had to refuse.'

Alec Jeffreys, the little known scientist from Leicester, was now becoming famous. He had put his discovery into the mainstream world and had achieved what so many of his colleagues dream about. It was to be a turning point but one that Jeffrey says was all down to luck. 'Had the Ghana boy case worked out differently, the first the public would have seen of DNA testing would have been a little lad seen kicking and screaming before being deported and flown back to Ghana. With hindsight, we were so lucky. First of all, immigration disputes are not legal disputes so you're not getting tied up with the full machinery of the law. And, secondly, it was science beating bureaucracy.'

This benign image of the new science continued when, shortly after the press coverage of his discovery, Jeffreys received a letter from the BBC asking him if he would take part in the popular children's TV programme, *Jim'll Fix It*. The idea behind the show was that children write in with requests to carry out things they'd never be able to do in normal life – fly fighter planes, swim with sharks, meet their favourite pop stars, that sort of thing. The host, former disc jockey Jimmy Saville, would then 'fix' it for their wishes to come true. Ten-year-old twins had written in to the show, saying that, although their mum believed they were identical, their Auntie Flo thought they weren't. Could Jim fix it for them to prove they were identical?

Professor Jeffreys was happy to oblige and, in front of an audience of millions of children and their parents, he produced DNA fingerprints for the girls confirming that they were, indeed, absolutely identical. For the jovial professor, it was an enjoyable experience. For the technique he had discovered, it was proof of how quickly a startling new discovery could be adopted by mainstream society.

Of course, immigration disputes were not the only type of paternity cases on the go. Behind closed doors, rather more salacious cases, involving illicit love affairs, spurned children and cheating husbands and wives, had been around since time began. Nowadays, when newspapers and magazines are full of stories of stars being caught out by science and having to own up to having fathered an illicit love child or two, it is hard to remember that, twenty or so years ago, these matters were confined to the nudge, nudge, wink, wink sections of society and the gossip columns.

Parenthood was easily denied because there was no guaranteed scientific method of determining it. Even the most hardline of judges had to concede that procreation was never a sure-fire process. Even if it had been proven without a shadow of doubt that sexual relations had taken place between two people, there was still no way of knowing, with absolute certainty, that the child in question was a result of that passionate moment. There were blood tests, of course, and they were used but, as was only too obvious – for example, from the likes of the Sarbah case – that their limitations were enormous.

The wealthy were usually advised that, with so many gold diggers and fraudsters on the scene, it was far smarter to deny parenthood of a child than simply assume that, just because sexual relations had taken place, a child had ensued. Naturally, after the publicity broke on the power of DNA fingerprinting, it wasn't long before the high-powered lawyers came knocking on the door of the quiet scientist from Leicester. The list of children who have been legally reunited with their famous fathers, as a result of Jeffreys' technique, is now so long that it alone could fill this book. But it's a little known fact that, in the first ever case of its type in the world, now protected by the laws of privacy, Alec Jeffreys found himself being accused in court of fathering an illicit child.

What a fantastic story it would be if the man who had discovered DNA fingerprinting actually found himself having to pay for his own indiscretions as a result of being caught by it. Before I find myself in the dock, accused of committing libel, I should point out right away that nothing could be further from the truth. Instead, a lawyer, faced with undisputable DNA evidence that his client was the father of a child whose paternity was in dispute, tried, as a last desperate throw of the dice, to deflect the blame away from his client and on to Alec Jeffreys.

The case involved an Englishwoman who hired a seventeen-year-old au pair to look after her child. Nothing unusual about that except that the au pair was male and French. The woman was divorced and attractive. 'Good on you!' her friends probably said as she cocked a snoot at convention. Unknown to them, at first, the relationship between the two was not strictly professional. As a result of a passionate moment, the Englishwoman became pregnant with, she said, her young au pair's child. Cue much cackling and 'I told you sos!' from friends no doubt. But there was a serious side to it. The child's alleged father denied point blank the baby was his and left the country at great haste to return to his own family in France. The family was not without money and, as the woman began a battle in the courts to have the child's father recognised and the financial responsibility accepted, they fought her every step of the way.

It was time to call on the services of Alec Jeffreys. The necessary tests were carried out and the results, once again, showed a positive match. The au pair was, Dr Jeffreys concluded, without a doubt the father of the child. The case went before a magistrate's court in late 1985. The judge accepted the scientific evidence and a decree was granted. Because of the laws protecting the anonymity of the child, this historically significant verdict did not make its way into the public domain.

'It was kind of fun – that case,' Jeffreys says. 'The magistrate's court in the UK had looked at the evidence and decreed the young man was the father. However, he had disappeared back to France. So the evidence was the put through a French court and they dithered and vacillated over it for . . . oh, I can't remember now – it was literally for years. There were all sorts of explanations of how the DNA fingerprints could match without him being the real father. Then I was told that the young man's lawyer had stood up in court in France and said that the whole thing had been a stitch up. He accepted the DNA was correct for the mum and correct for the child but he wouldn't accept it was correct for the young man. He claimed that the only person who could legitimately be the father was the person who had tested the DNA and that was me!'

Jeffreys roars with laughter as he tells this tale. 'It was an interesting concept but I'd never ever met this woman in my life. It was suggested I sue but I just thought this was such a wonderful story. At the end of the day, the French court accepted that the au pair was the child's father. And that was the case that started the whole paternity thing rolling.'

And that was the state of play in Alec Jeffreys' Leicestershire lab when the police came knocking with that speculative phone call. The lab was already knee deep in paternity cases – some were immigration disputes and others were more to do with sexual shenanigans. As Jeffreys freely admits, he and his staff were becoming overwhelmed. It is all the more surprising, then, that he took the phone call that was to divert his technique into a new field and unleash a terrifyingly accurate forensic tool on criminals the world over. It was also, of course, to open a can of worms.

3

THE BEGINNING

Just who made the phone call to Alec Jeffreys' lab that afternoon has long been the subject of some debate. Richard Buckland's father is on record as saying he asked his lawyer to do it. But the police are pretty confident it was their idea. Alec Jeffreys can't remember. He does know it wasn't the man in charge of the murder hunt, Chief Superintendent David Baker. Mr Baker agrees with him on that. But, like Jeffreys, he's absolutely sure the call came from a police officer. Mr Baker's memory is a bit fuzzy on the subject – it was, after all, a minor detail – but he believes that he asked Peter Lehome, one of his senior officers to check out the scientist at the local lab who was working on DNA. Baker had read about Jeffreys' breakthrough in the local newspaper and noticed speculation that it could, one day, be used to help solve crime. Intrigued by the fact that the suspect he had in custody for the Enderby murders had only confessed to the second of the two murders, he was casting about for a way to confirm his involvement in the first. He contacted the Home Office to ask if the Jeffreys technique was officially available and could be used. The Home Office dashed his hopes pretty quickly. 'They said "No". It was at least two years down the line,' he recalls. 'So that was really that. But I had read about Alec Jeffreys being local so we gave him a try anyway.'

The problem, as Mr Baker freely admits, was that Buckland had nothing whatsoever to say about the first murder. 'We were reasonably convinced that whoever had done the second had done the first,' Mr Baker says. 'The blood tests matched but they weren't very discriminating. That's why we went down the DNA route.'

Going down the DNA route involved another complication. The crime scene samples taken from the two murders were the property of the Crown and would be extremely important productions during the forthcoming trial. The way such key items are handled could mean the

41

a prosecution case succeeding or going crashing
nbarrassment. The samples were not even stored
re Constabulary. The Chief Superintendent was
ask of persuading the Whitehall mandarins to
uvely obscure scientist who would be subjecting
all sorts of possibly damaging procedures. Surprisingly he
succeeded.

Of course, Professor Jeffreys had already agreed to try to help the police but he really wasn't fully aware of what he was getting into. His wake-up call came when the biological samples arrived in his labs. After the roller coaster ride of the previous year, when every day seemed to dawn to a wider horizon, this was to be a sobering experience.

'You have got this dyed-in-the-wool academic,' he says, 'and then suddenly you have these samples turn up – a sample of blood from the accused, a sample of pubic hair from the victims. I realised, "Oh, my God! This is real. This is for real. This isn't messing about with chemicals any more. This is a human tragedy." I found that difficult. I could cope with it but it was hard.'

The contrast from the work he had previously been involved in couldn't have been more startling. 'With immigration disputes, you're helping people. With paternity disputes, sometimes the people involved are sort of risqué. You don't get that sort of empathy somehow. With forensics, we were suddenly in a different league. And I wasn't a forensic scientist. I hadn't been used to handling that sort of stuff. I hadn't been used to thinking about what was happening in these terrible assaults. It hit home quite deep.'

But Professor Jeffreys' troubles were only just beginning. He was aware, as was the Home Office, that the standards required for criminal work were extremely high. There had been preliminary discussions about it long before Leicestershire Constabulary came calling and it had been agreed that the testing system he had pioneered was not going to be sophisticated or robust enough to withstand the full scrutiny of the law.

Nonetheless, important steps were being taken to transform DNA fingerprinting into a crime-fighting tool. Nobody was saying it would never happen. It was just a long way away. One of those steps involved the Home Office scientist, Dr Peter Gill. Part of the problem with DNA fingerprinting was that it was brilliant with nice fresh samples of blood, which contain big dollops of genetic material. Unfortunately, it was next to useless with anything other than that. It wasn't the technique that was at fault – it was simply that nobody had come up with a method of reliably extracting DNA from anything other than the best samples.

Of course, as everybody was painfully aware at the time, criminals were rarely considerate enough to leave fresh blood at the scene and, even when they did, it was often hours or even days before it was discovered, rendering the evidence useless. There was another problem as well. In sexual crimes, such as rape, there could be DNA material available in the form of semen but, yet again, there was no reliable way of extracting that material. Even when the semen could be seen and collected, it might be so thoroughly mixed in with the victim's DNA that it was impossible to separate the two and get a clear result. Test after test on such samples had failed to come up with anything remotely resembling a clear result.

Enter stage left Dr Peter Gill and his Home Office colleague, Dave Werret (Mr Werret would go on to head the Forensic Science Service's National DNA Database but, at this point of time, all that was years ahead). Gill and Werret went to Jeffreys' Leicestershire lab for a period of four weeks to examine the techniques used and then they returned to their own lab at Aldermaston to try to come up with a method of increasing the range of samples that DNA could be extracted from.

'No one had ever tried to analyse dried blood samples before,' says Dr Gill. 'And all of the scientists we spoke to said it would be too difficult. They said it wouldn't work because the blood would be unstable.' Remarkably, after much trial and error, the scientists achieved what they had set out to do with dried blood cells and then moved on to the second problem.

'We couldn't separate vaginal and sperm cells,' Dr Gill recalls. 'There were just so many vaginal cells that they absolutely swamped the sperm cells. We tried to do it but it just wouldn't work. We had to think very carefully about extraction methodology.'

Eventually, they came up with a clever technique which revolved around the fact that sperm cells are extremely tough. By washing the two different types of cells in a detergent, they managed to sweep away the vaginal cells. 'They just exploded,' says Dr Gill. The next step was to take the residue, turn it into pellets and then wash it with a detergent again. They were left with solely sperm cells. The tough outer shell of sperm, which had proved so durable in surviving the detergent, then became a problem. How could they get rid of it to get to the DNA inside with destroying the sensitive contents?

The answer was to bathe the samples in a chemical that broke down the tough sulphurous barriers that made up the outer casing. It was tried and it worked. The DNA inside survived the bathing and over-night the range of materials that could be used to DNA fingerprint someone or something had enlarged enormously. It seemed like a small step but, in fact, it was enormously significant. The results were reported in *Nature*.

So, serious progress was being made but there really was no way that anybody in their right mind could have thought that DNA finger-printing was ready to be unleashed on to the world of crime fighting. The tests took a long time and there was still a large number of grey areas around the edges which had not been explored. Why did Jeffreys say 'Yes' to Leicester-shire Constabulary, then? The professor is not too sure about that. It could have been that he approached everything with a positive open mind and walking away from challenges was not in his nature. After all, that's how he got involved in paternity testing. Or it could have been that Leicestershire Police were not really asking for that much. They had a confession and it was obvious to everybody the same person had carried out both murders so there would be no harm in trying to match the samples.

The first decision taken by the team was that DNA fingerprinting wasn't the tool for the job. Fingerprinting was an astonishingly powerful tool – too powerful, maybe. Those blocky patterns produced in the photographs carried an extremely high level of detail. To be frank, there was too much information. Comparing two different samples and trying to match them was difficult and could be seen as subjective. Something easier to understand and less complex was called for.

They decided to use a system, called DNA profiling, which they had just developed. Essentially, this was a simplification of the finger-printing technique and produced the results in vertical bands that were easy to compare with others. What the technique lacked in complexity it more than made up for in clarity.

Back in those days, the amount of DNA material available was crucial to the success of the test. A sizeable amount – enough, say, to cover an old two-shilling piece – was about the minimum that was practical. The bigger the dollop of sample material available, the quicker the test was and the clearer the result would be. Jeffreys' team had already discovered that, when the sample material wasn't good enough, the photographs that developed were too weak, too faint to be of any use. It was a case of the bigger the sample, the quicker the testing and the better the photograph of the code.

When Dr Jeffreys and his colleagues opened the envelopes containing the samples from the two murders, they spotted a problem right away. There was more material available from the Lynda Mann murder than there was from Dawn Ashworth's. And, when they tested the samples, only the ones from Lynda Mann's case came out properly. The Ashworth murder samples were too faint and they had to be retested.

While that was happening, Jeffreys and his team got down to the job of comparing the good profile from the murder of Lynda Mann with the profile of the accused. The result was a bit of a shocker. It was certainly a surprise to Jeffreys and an even bigger surprise to the police. The profiles did not match. The sample taken from Buckland was not the same as the one taken from Lynda. It seemed the reason Buckland had not confessed to the first murder was simply because he didn't do it. Dr Jeffreys phoned Chief Superintendent Baker to break the news. 'I told him,' Jeffreys recalls, 'I can't say anything about the second case yet but, in the first case, it looks as if it was someone else. There was a . . . disappointed response shall we say.'

It has to be remembered that the whole point of the exercise was to tie young Buckland to the first murder so this was a setback. 'Oh, yes,' Jeffreys recalls. 'The police thought they had their man. Our remit was to confirm his involvement in the second murder to which he had confessed and see if he was responsible for the first murder as well. That was precisely it.'

Still the police consoled themselves with the thought that the tests were still taking place on the samples taken from Dawn and, when they came through, the confirmation would help their case.

A week later, the results were ready. 'That's when I began to get really worried,' says Jeffreys. 'It wasn't Buckland.' Far from confirming Buckland had carried out the first murder, which had been the whole point of the exercise, DNA profiling had actually cleared him of both. And there was yet another shocking development. It was crystal clear from the DNA profile that the same person – some unknown person – had carried out the first murder and the second murder. The profiles were absolutely indistinguishable. A chill ran down Jeffreys' spine. If these results were correct, he and his colleagues were the only people to know that an entirely innocent man was languishing in prison and a double murderer was on the loose.

'I was worried because the police were convinced they had the right man,' he recalls.

To say the result was a bombshell was putting it mildly. Chief Superintendent Baker remembers muttering an oath when he was told over the telephone. Alec Jeffreys remembers hearing something 'distinctly Anglo Saxon' coming down the phone. Dr Jeffreys was now under immense pressure. Was he right? 'Well, either the murderer was still out there or there was something fundamentally wrong with our technology,' he remembers. On his say-so, an innocent man could be set free and the hunt or a double murderer resumed. Or, if he had got it wrong, a killer could be set free into the community. It was a terrible dilemma.

'We thought, "Oh, God! This doesn't work.",' Jeffreys says. 'We then did an additional test and got exactly the same result. When I told the police, their first reaction was the same as mine – there was something seriously wrong with the technology.'

A crisis meeting was called. It was held in Jeffreys' lab and was attended by Home Office scientists, Chief Superintendent Baker and Dr Jeffreys. Everybody pored over the information, seeking a way out of the impasse. The worry at the front of everyone's mind was whether they were actually comparing like for like. The suspect's DNA had been extracted from blood. The samples from the murder scenes were taken from semen. Was it possible that one person's DNA profile could vary between their semen and their blood?

The science was so new that nobody really knew. This, of course, was one of the reasons that the Home Office had not been keen to rush into it. Of course, there was another reason but that wouldn't emerge for a year or so.

Anyway, Jeffreys himself was unsure. 'We couldn't think of any biological explanation for why the DNA profile from one person should be totally different in the semen sample compared to blood. It just didn't make sense at all. We compared blood and semen on a number of other people and, of course, they matched. We all pored over the information we had.'

Was it all a screw-up? Jeffreys is honest enough to concede that, in those emotionally charged hours, he did not believe his own results. Neither did the police. During that afternoon, the fate of his new science, not to mention the future of a possibly innocent young man, hung in the balance. If they had stopped there and then and walked away from DNA profiling on the grounds it wasn't ready, nobody would have been surprised. Young Buckland would still be tried on the basis of his tape-recorded confession and other corroborating factors that the police felt were important to the case. All the officers involved were sure they would get a conviction anyway. They would not have rock-solid proof that he had carried out the first murder but work could continue on that.

Dr Jeffreys now agrees he would have been willing to walk away from the results if the whole room had been against them. 'That was the way I was playing it,' he says. 'I wasn't saying, "This is iron-clad technology.". I was agonising. But I was thinking this has got to be right. I racked my brains over how a DNA profile could differ between sperm and blood. We could accidentally release a double murderer if we got this wrong. Obviously it was a responsibility.'

But they didn't abandon the tests. It was the scientists from the Home Office who refused to accept they were wrong. Dave Werret was at the meeting and argued strongly in favour of Jeffreys' results. He said, Jeffreys recalls, 'I'm sorry but these results really look compelling.' His intervention won the day and was to have an extremely significant impact on the future of DNA fingerprinting.

It was agreed that further tests would be carried out separately by the Home Office to check Jeffreys' results. This time the tests would switch back to the original method of DNA fingerprinting. It was the only technique the Home Office scientists were familiar with. Then they ran into another problem.

DNA fingerprinting and its updated equivalent DNA profiling had been patented by the Lister Institute, the charity that sponsored Jeffreys' work. Despite the desperate efforts by Jeffreys' team to keep their new discovery secret until the patents had been published, the tom-toms had been beating. The international giant ICI pricked up its ears and came calling on Jeffreys and the Lister Institute. In conditions of the greatest secrecy, they thrashed out a licensing deal which would give them exclusive international rights to the new technology. It was signed before the patents were made public. To exploit the new development, a company called Cellmark Diagnostics was created and set up at Abingdon in Oxfordshire.

Its permission had to be sought to reproduce the experiment. It would not be the first time in the coming weeks that the company would be faced with the question of whether to put commercial advantage before justice. In fact, things were to move so rapidly that even commercial might would be unable to stand in the way of the new science.

The new tests were carried out by the Home Office scientists at Aldermaston. In the days and weeks that followed, the atmosphere in Jeffreys' lab was tense. Dr Jeffreys knew that the credibility of his technique, not to mention his own reputation, would be affected by the outcome.

Eventually the call came through. The Home Office scientists had come up with the same result as Jeffreys' lab. 'There was a sigh of relief on my part,' Jeffreys says. 'The conclusion we initially came to – that this guy was the wrong bloke – was right.' And, at that point, the police accepted it too. Buckland was released from prison. He had become the first person in the world cleared by DNA typing.

Chief Superintendent Baker was now faced with an astonishing situation. He had gone to the new science to try to secure a second murder charge against someone who had already confessed to one murder. Not only did that fail, he also saw the value of his original evidence wiped out with one little test result. His suspect had been cleared and had walked free. He was back to square one in the hunt for a double murderer that the whole nation was watching intently. The pressure was enormous.

Such a setback would have embittered many men. It could even, in other circumstances, have led to a reshuffle of personnel – a new man at the top and a new investigation. But Mr Baker stayed on the case. What he did next was to launch DNA fingerprinting on an unsuspecting world and set in motion a sequence of events that would have an enormous impact on policing the world over. Even Dr Jeffreys would call it 'a real act of faith' and a step of 'enormous bravery'.

Mr Baker sat down and decided that the only thing he had left from the hundreds of hours of police work that had gone into the enquiry was the DNA profile of the assailant. He decided, therefore, to DNA-test virtually a whole community.

The story of that extraordinary exercise has been immortalised in the book *The Blooding* by Joseph Wambaugh. It gives an incredibly detailed blow-by-blow account of the subsequent chase and capture of the real killer. Naturally, because of its historical significance, the Enderby murder case, has become one of the most written about in British crime history with literally scores of newspaper articles across the globe teasing out its tiniest details.

It began, says the chief superintendent, with yet another discussion with Cellmark Diagnostics. The problem was that each DNA test would cost in the region of £100. Given that thousands of possible suspects were going to be examined, the overall cost was way out of the police's league – even for a murder inquiry of this magnitude. Chief Super-intendent Baker began the new investigation by calling his officers together and announcing to them, 'We're going to try something that has never been done before.'

His decision was prompted by the realisation that conventional policing was running out of ideas. 'If we pursued conventional means that we'd pursued to that time, there would be no guarantee that we were going to get a result. So, you know, what we needed was this new technology to work for us and see if we could get one individual with the same blood type and DNA match.' On 2 January 1987, the press were told that something 'revolutionary' was going to be tried in an attempt to track down the double killer.

Despite the fact that no agreement had yet been struck with Cellmark and no fees were being paid to the company, the exercise was still going to be enormously expensive. Doctors had to be paid £36 an hour to take blood. Photographs had to be taken of all the suspects who could not provide their own photographic identification. And tens of thousands of miles would be racked up criss-crossing the country to test people who had been in the murder area at the time.

For that reason, the police officers involved in the inquiry worked without being paid for overtime. Initially, every male, living in the area and aged between seventeen and thirty-four (the age at which it was thought the sperm count would have dropped below the level of that left by the killer) at the time of Lynda Mann's murder in 1983, would be tested. In addition, men, who hadn't resided in the villages but had been there on business, holiday, for health reasons or whatever, were to be examined too. Then it was increased to include all men born between 1 January 1953 and 31 December 1970. Eventually, all men in that age category, whether alibied or not, would undergo the process. It would bring about 4,000 people into the enquiry.

Letters were sent out inviting people to attend either the screenings to be held three nights a week between 7 p.m. and 9 p.m. or a single day session held between 9.30 a.m. and 11 a.m. It was a Herculean task. On arriving at the testing stations, every man was interviewed by a police officer to establish their movements during the two days in question. Forms were to be filled in, identification produced and, as was the case with the vast majority of those attending, photographs were to be taken of anyone without passports or other photo ID.

The samples were sent to a laboratory in Huntingdon for initial screening. If, and only if, they matched the blood class PGM 1 +, a secretor that the police knew was the killer's group, the samples would then be sent on to Aldermaston for DNA testing. Within weeks, a huge backlog began to build up. It was the first time in the world that this kind of testing had ever been done on such a scale and it was inevitable the fledgling system would struggle to cope. Soon Aldermaston scientists were begging for the most interesting samples to be labelled 'urgent'. They could then bump these up to the front of the queue and this would lessen the number of irritated requests from police officers, demanding to know why a key suspect's DNA result wasn't appearing.

But that wasn't the real flaw in the system. The real flaw was that coming forward for screening was completely voluntary. Nobody could be compelled to give blood. Naturally, the police used the newspapers to make it crystal clear that, although they couldn't compel someone to give blood, they would be extremely suspicious of people who didn't. Wives, girlfriends and mothers were all urged to persuade their men to attend for testing so that they could clear themselves. And they did. Many women urged their partners to go along to the testing stations and, in one instance, a woman actually dragged her boyfriend along and told police to make sure they test him. They did and he was cleared – as were hundreds of others as the results rolled in. By May, 3,600 men had been tested and DNA sampling had cleared 2,000 of those. But, all the time, the police team was facing cutbacks and the number of officers involved in the inquiry had dwindled to twenty-four. In all, ninety-eight per cent of those the police wanted to test had come forward and volunteered to be tested. That left two per cent who still had to be tracked down. But, as the resources shrunk, the scale of the inquiry seemed to get bigger and bigger. Every day new leads brought more people into the screening database, increasing the original numbers dramatically. Five months after screening started, there were still 1,000 more men to be put to the test.

The realisation that any murderer with more than half a brain would not voluntarily put himself forward to give blood was gnawing away at everybody. But, in terms of keeping the murders in the public eye, the exercise had initially been a tremendous success. News teams from all over the world had flown in to film the extraordinary scenes that were taking place in the three villages. One Italian film crew even captured one man swooning into the arms of an officer at the sight of his own blood. But, by the time the first anniversary of Dawn Ashworth's death came around on 31 July 1987, it was becoming a struggle to keep the impetus going.

At that time, the gardener in the little village graveyard in Enderby would have behaved much like the current one does in nearby Narborough cemetery. He would be polite, chatty, maybe even show visitors to Dawn's grave if they asked. He would stand by the gravestone bearing the inscription 'Treasured memories of our dear daughter' and shake his head at the waste of a young life. Unlike the caretaker at Narborough graveyard, he wasn't a council employee or even paid by the parish church. The gardener was a police officer, named Phil

Beeken, who had been detailed to keep a close watch on all those who visited the cemetery on the anniversary of the young girl's death. Phil Beeken's eyes weren't the only pair watching the comings and goings in the Enderby cemetery. The police had also installed a surveillance camera on her grave through which they watched everything with great interest. On the day after Dawn's anniversary, Phil Beeken was there mowing and tending and watching and the camera was silently capturing time-lapse images of the grave for other enquiry team officers to watch. Unknown to them, on exactly that very day, something was taking place a few miles away in nearby Leicester that would eventually solve the murder. Long after his gardening duties had ended and six weeks into the future, Phil Beeken would take a phone call which would signal the sudden beginning of the end for the murder enquiry. That phone call would be sparked by a conversation that was taking place in the Clarendon Pub in Leicester.

Nowadays the Tabasco Jazz, the Orange Tree and the Revolution are *the* places in Leicester to be seen in and to drink in. Twenty years ago, the Clarendon was up there with the best of them. It wasn't that trendy but it had the kind of mixed clientele that gives a bar a sort of cachet. Journalists drank there – as did students, lecturers and ordinary everyday punters. Ordinary punters like bakery shop workers. Bakery shop workers from the Hampshires Bakery shop just up the road. It was Saturday afternoon and there, in one of the banquettes, three bakery workers were having a pint and a filled roll for their lunch. They were talking about one of their colleagues, a married man, named Colin, who'd got a girl pregnant. It was the sort of juicy stuff most people enjoy indulging in, even if they don't directly know the person involved. Only two of the people knew this guy, Colin, they were talking about. One of those two, a young man, named Ian Kelly had an even juicier snippet to impart. Leaning over to his colleagues, he said, 'Colin asked me take the blood test for him.' The only woman in the company, the woman who managed the bakery, said, 'What test?' The other chap said, 'The murder inquiry test?' Then a strange thing happened. Ian got up to go to the bar and the other man leaned over to her and said, 'Colin asked me to do it too. He offered me £200 to take the blood test. He's scared of coppers. A weird bloke.'

The bakery manager was uncertain about what she had heard. She was so unsure that she didn't go to the police with her information. She spoke to one of the young men again and he told her to 'leave it'. 'Was there anything sinister in it?' she wondered. Or was it simply a lads' thing that she should keep out of. She didn't want to get this Colin into serious trouble over nothing. But it preyed on her mind. Instead of just walking into a police station, she decided to put a filter between herself and the police. She would tell a policeman she knew – the son of the man who owned the Clarendon Pub. But it turned out he was on holiday. So she put it to the back of her mind for a while. But it wouldn't go away. Six weeks later, she rang him up and told him about the conversation.

On 18 September, Phil Beeken, back in the office, answered a call from a policeman. The full details of the pub conversation, the offered money and the claim that Ian Kelly had acted as a substitute for a work colleague, whose name was Colin Pitchfork, were relayed to him. It didn't take long to pull Pitchfork's file to check the signature he'd offered on a routine doorstep police inquiry against the signature held against the blood sample. They didn't match. It didn't take long either to knock on Ian Kelly's door, put the fear of God in him and have him confessing rapidly that he had taken the test for a certain Colin Pitchfork who lived in Hayburn Close just on the edge of Narborough. Kelly said he had only taken the test to help Pitchfork out because Pitchfork had already acted as a substitute for someone else and couldn't take the test himself.

Kelly said later, 'He kept pestering and pestering and the reason he gave me was he'd done it for somebody else. And he'd got two kids. I kept saying, "No, no, no." I felt sorry for his kids. I'd been ill. I was on antibiotics. I felt so rough, I weren't interested. I was worried that what I was doing was wrong. But I hadn't got any clue that he had involved in it or anything.'

On Sunday 20 September, the police were waiting outside Colin Pitchfork's house as he and his family drove up in their blue Fiat. The police had come the day before but the family had been away. Pitchfork's wife, Carole, answered the door initially thinking, as she'd later say, that it was two insurance men who were standing before her. By then, the house was surrounded by police. Once the police had identified themselves, there was no mucking about. Pitchfork was taken to the kitchen of the house where Officer Mick Thomas said, 'We believe you are responsible for the murder of Dawn Ashworth on 31 July 1986. We believe another man gave a blood sample for you. I'm arresting you on the suspicion of that murder. I must inform you that you don't have to say anything but anything you say may be taken down and given in evidence. Do you understand?'

Minutes later Carole, stunned to learn that the negative results of the blood test sent to her husband had actually been for another man, asked him straight out, 'Did you do it?' 'Yes,' Pitchfork said. In the ensuing melee, as Mrs Pitchfork flew at her lying, cheating, murdering husband, one police officer received a punch in the face and a kick in the groin. But that didn't dampen the incredible surge of elation that went through the whole team at the capture of the man they'd been seeking for so long.

Within hours, the tale of Colin Pitchfork, a two-bit womaniser with a history of flashing and a psychopathic tendency, came tumbling out in all its horror and tragedy. As he sat in the police interview room and insisted on retelling his life story from the age of seven, sordid details poured out about a life of petty sexual crime, public infidelity and then two brutal murders. This time, there was no possible dubiety about who the police had before them. Like the grand master taking centre stage, Pitchfork relished the attention and, in precise detail, he recounted every minute of the deaths of Dawn Ashworth and Lynda Mann. And it was the sheer pettiness of his motive for murder – the breathtakingly ordinariness of the reasons he gave for killing – that were the most shocking. Pitchfork told police that he had murdered young Lynda Mann because she had noticed he wore a wedding ring and asked, 'What about your wife?' That was it. Four words uttered by an extremely brave and intelligent young girl. Because of that, he said, her life was snuffed out. For nothing more than a pervert's fear he would be exposed through his family. When it came to Dawn's murder, he claimed that he had only killed her because she had failed to step past him when he flashed at her. Of course, these excuses were the delusion and justifications of an extremely sick mind. But how sickening that Pitchfork could believe such statements could somehow explain what he had done.

Pitchfork also revealed that, many times, he'd considered murdering

Ian Kelly, the bakery worker who gave him his way out. But he reasoned that could draw too much attention to himself. After all, he had had to ask quite a few people to take his blood test for him before he found someone stupid enough to do it.

On 22 January 1988, Colin Pitchfork was sentenced at Leicester Crown Court. He was twenty-seven years old. The prosecuting counsel, Mr Brian Escott Cox QC, said Pitchfork had been fully aware of the dangers of DNA fingerprinting and had gone out of his way to avoid it. 'It became clear to Pitchfork that the police had a deadly weapon for the detection of crime,' he said. 'He had to find some way to get out of it without drawing attention to himself.' He recounted to the court how Pitchfork skilfully altered his passport by placing Kelly's photograph on it, how he had drilled details of his family into Kelly and how he had persuaded the twenty-three-year-old to practise forging his signature until he got it off perfectly.

'It worked,' added Mr Escott Cox. 'Kelly went in and carried it off. The Crown does, however, accept that he did not know he was doing it for the guilty man.'

The counsel went on to tell the court that, out of the thousands of people the police had lined up to test, only two men had refused to give samples. One had a genuine excuse and the other was Pitchfork. 'DNA is a miraculously wonderful process. It is a tremendous advance in the detection of crime.'

Pitchfork pleaded guilty to all charges. His counsel added, 'He will remain forever haunted by the images and knowledge of what he has done.'

In passing sentence, the judge, Mr Justice Otton, referred to a psychiatrist's report, compiled at Broadmoor, which described Pitchfork as a 'psychopath of a psychosexual type'.

Pitchfork got a double life sentence for the murders, ten years for each rape, three years for two other sexual assaults the police had uncovered and three years for the conspiracy with Ian Kelly to avoid the blood tests. Pitchfork's sentences were to run concurrently. Unusually, in a murder case of such an appalling nature, the judge did not recommend a minimum sentence, meaning Pitchfork could have been out in the minimum period of just twelve years.

Ian Kelly was given a suspended two-year sentence for conspiracy to pervert the course of justice. The families were there to watch. Lynda Mann's stepfather, Eddie Eastwood, said, 'I just wanted to see his face. I wanted to know what sort of man could do it . . . . I couldn't make him out. He looked almost human.' Barbara Ashworth, Dawn's mum, said, 'I had to lay the ghost to rest.'

Although it was mentioned at the trial, the DNA evidence played no role in Pitchfork's conviction. He had confessed in his house, he had later confessed at the police station and he pled guilty in court so there was no need for it. In the months that it took for Pitchfork to appear in court, the world of DNA fingerprinting had moved on. Even if it had been necessary to present that evidence to the court, Pitchfork would not have been the first person to be convicted on its strength.

In November 1987, Robert Melias, a thirty-two-year-old labourer, was convicted at Bristol Crown Court of rape on the basis of his genetic fingerprint. There was no great fuss made about the historic case. The public were growing used to DNA fingerprinting. And the day before Pitchfork was sentenced, a man, whose identity was not made public to protect his victim, was found guilty at the Old Bailey of raping his eleven-year-old stepdaughter. He made legal history by pleading not guilty, undergoing a jury trial and being convicted on DNA evidence. The evidence revealed that the child born to his stepdaughter was his.

A year later, there was an interesting footnote to the Pitchfork murders. In September 1988, the Home Office confirmed that it had paid an undisclosed figure in compensation to ICI for unauthorised use of the genetic fingerprint test whose exclusive rights were owned by Cellmark Diagnostics. It turned out nobody had ever actually obtained that permission from Cellmark to fingerprint those thousands of males in Narborough, Enderby and Littlethorpe. A spokesman defended the decision saying, 'There was a public need to find the criminal, the technology was available and we could not afford to delay.' It hadn't just been Alec Jeffreys or Chief Superintendent Baker who had been going out on a limb to catch Colin Pitchfork. The government had been at it too. Bravo.

4

KRAZY KARY

What were the chances of a DNA fingerprinting test being wrong? Billions-to-one. The world was told that the statistical levels of accuracy were quite simply staggering. The test was, like the pope, clearly infallible – not only infallible, but soon-to-be universally applicable. As part of the deal thrashed out with the Home Office, Cellmark publicly announced it would be carrying out all future mass screenings organised by the police. So there would be more Enderbys. The company would also be training Home Office scientists to do scene-of-crime testing, using kits supplied solely by them. There was even talk of a nationwide deployment of forensic probes by a government that was now swooning over the new wonder technology. The public woke up to discover that the future had arrived overnight. It seemed like every police officer would be going round with a pocket-sized Sherlock Homes at his or her disposal, just waiting to be unleashed on defenceless criminals. Everybody was seduced by Dr Alec Jeffreys' sensational discovery. Millions of words were written on how the game was up for the killers and the rapists, the burglars and the paedophiles.

Unfortunately, the truth was a bit more sobering than that. Yes, DNA fingerprinting was sensational, yes, it could provide dizzying levels of accuracy but, no, it wasn't suitable for general use. Behind the initial euphoria, the grey facts were that DNA tests were difficult to conduct, insensitive and extremely slow to yield results. Great if there was a limitless supply of DNA material from the victims, fantastic if the suspects were known and could be coerced into giving large dollops of blood or other DNA material but pretty hopeless in other situations. It could take up to twenty stages to get a result for just one sample and, for much of the time, it took weeks to ensure complete accuracy. Scientists had to stand around waiting for chemical reactions to take place and frozen photographs to develop. The hard fact was that the test that had changed the scientific world, DNA fingerprinting, just wasn't going to cut the mustard in the real world. It was too slow and too awkward. Even its offspring, DNA profiling, was a million miles away from being a universally applicable police tool. Speed was what the police initially wanted – speed and the ability to carry out testing on smaller samples. The search for these two factors, the Holy Grail of forensic lab work, would take more than a decade to complete. And, although the bewitched public didn't realise it, with every new refinement of Alex Jeffreys' invention – and there were to be many – the degree of accuracy of the results would tumble. Nobody was hiding anything, of course. In fact, the real-life limitations of the technology were graphically revealed only months after the Enderby case when the first ever murder to be solved using DNA profiling came to court. By then, of course, the world had gone DNA mad and nobody was playing a blind bit of notice to its limited applicability.

History has a way of seeking out the strangest places to leave its indelible mark. In early 1988, just after the people of Leicester had seen Colin Pitchfork jailed for life, the focus of Home Office attention switched to another small village – this time in rural Lancashire. It was the case with no body – the murder with no witness. It should have taken an eternity to solve but, instead, the police found the murderer with no motive dropping straight into their arms.

There is a poem, by W H Auden, which contains the following lines:

> But all the clocks in the city
> Began to whirr and chime:
> 'O let not Time deceive you,
> You cannot conquer Time.'

If the clocks in the little village of Billinge had started to whirr and chime at 5.15 p.m. on Tuesday 9 February 1998, they could not have marked the dividing line between a life lived and a life lost more clearly. At 5.15 p.m., a young woman, in the prime of her life, stepped off a bus a few hundred yards from her home and vanished into the wintry night, never to be seen again. Helen McCourt's disappearance was not quiet or unnoticed – she had family and friends who cared for her – and people she had spoken to not long before. Her mother,

Marie, for example, who was waiting at home for Helen to get off that bus from Liverpool, where she worked, and come home for her tea. People like her boyfriend who expected to go out with her that evening. When twenty-two-year-old Helen didn't arrive, these people worried, they phoned the police, they raised the alarm.

The next morning, fifteen miles away, a butcher, out walking his dog along the towpath of the Manchester Ship Canal, noticed a bloody white towel. Gordon Bannister stopped to look at it and then he noticed another one on an embankment and a full set of male clothing – a sweater with a Labatt's beer logo, jeans that someone had just stepped out of, underpants and socks. They were all covered in blood.

A missing girl, a pile of bloody clothes. What was going on? The next morning, Thursday morning, the police were tracing Helen's route from the point where her fellow passengers had seen her get off the bus to her home. They got as far as the George and Dragon. Helen drank there from time to time. Most young people drank there from time to time. It was a rough and tough place, popular with local lads and run by a former Pilkington's glass factory worker, Ian Simms. Simms had been a popular shop steward in the factory but had given it up when the tenancy of the pub in his local village became available. He became a pretty popular licensee. He could hold his own with the locals, have a laugh and would even run some of them home on occasion. Of course, the police knew him. Most people knew him. He was out when they initially arrived but he returned around 11.35 a.m. as they were still conducting their enquiries. A police officer started asking Simms routine questions like whether he had seen anything and where had he just been. Simms said he'd just returned from a visit to the British Legion Club in the nearby village of Irlam. He wanted to put on exotic dancing evenings there. But it was waste of time. There had been nobody in.

The officer couldn't help noticing Ian Simms was behaving pretty strangely. His stomach was heaving, literally, and he seemed, the policeman later said, to be palpitating with fear. Naturally, he was asked to come along to the police station in St Helen's, the nearest town, and make a statement. While he was there his Volkswagen car was searched. Forensic scientists took part of an earring away. It was shown to Helen McCourt's mother. She said it was just like one of her daughter's. Ian Simms was charged with her murder on Friday 12 February.

If police were worried that the evidence against the man they'd charged seemed pretty circumstantial, they didn't have long to wait until their concerns were assuaged. Within a month, they were cordoning off an area of land, a couple of miles outside the village, where a PT instructor, out shooting rats, had discovered a handbag containing credit cards. The bag was Helen's and it was surrounded by a mountain of evidence. A black bin bag contained her clothes. There was also a grey jacket lying beside it and a piece of electrical flex, which had been twisted into a noose-like shape.

When the grey jacket was shown to Ian Simms in his police cell, he immediately pointed at the torn cuff and said it belonged to him. Astonishingly, he also pointed to bite marks on the flex, said they had been made by his dog and confirmed it was from his bar. Things were stacking up against the pub landlord.

Ian Simms was a bit of a wild lad with a reputation in Billinge for living it up. He stayed around the corner from the pub, with his wife and family, but had a flat upstairs where he conducted a secret-ish affair with his nineteen-year-old girlfriend. It was something he'd managed to keep from his wife but others knew about it and tongues were beginning to wag. In fact, at the time of his arrest, Ian Simms believed that someone was going to tell his wife about what he'd been up to. The worry over that formed part of his alibi for the evening Helen McCourt had disappeared. He said he'd driven through the wintry weather to Southport to think things over about his life.

After the second batch of clothes was found, things went rapidly downhill for Ian Simms. With Simms in police custody, his pub was now boarded-up and the police returned to the premises to conduct a more thorough examination. They found the other half of Helen's earring, the butterfly clip, in Simms' flat above the pub. A local jeweller testified he'd made the earrings. It got worse. A clump of hair found inside Simms' grey coat pocket – the grey coat he had immediately admitted was his – turned out to be from Helen. The sweatshirt, that had been found at the canal-side, had blood on it and also bore the logo of Labatt's Beer. Ian Simms sold a lot of Labatt's beer in his pub and he had been heard saying he couldn't get enough of their promotional clothes.

It went on. Fibres found on Helen's coat matched those from the carpet on the pub floor and they appeared to have been embedded there when the coat was 'in forcible' contact with the pub floor. Fibres from the boot of Simms' car were linked with Helen and fibres from one of her mittens were found on his coat.

There was still no body, though. Nor was there anything, apart from the hair, to link Helen with foul play. The blood samples taken from the found clothes had been sent to the Home Office forensic lab at Aldermaston and tested. They were subjected to DNA fingerprinting, using the original multi-locus probe system developed by Jeffreys. Multi-locus probes, in simple terms, test DNA from a variety of sites and produce big, square bar-code patterns. They are stunningly accurate simply because there is so much DNA material shown in the result. However, in this case, they didn't work. The dreaded weakness – the lack of enough material to give a result – had struck. The blood samples were simply too degraded to be of any use. It was decided to submit them to a new DNA test, called the single-locus probe, that was in the process of being developed. This had the advantage of being quicker than the old multi-locus probe system and being far more sensitive to smaller amounts of material. It could deal with samples half the size of the old test and still return a decent result. Instead of going in and grabbing a huge amount of DNA to sample, as was the case with DNA fingerprinting, specific areas were targeted they produced double bar patterns. This made the results much easier to compare and they worked.

There was a problem in that Helen McCourt had never given blood. This meant there was no DNA available from her to compare with the stuff found in the pub and on the clothes. It was not an insurmountable difficulty. Using a similar technique as had been used in the Andrew Sarbah case, the scientists took blood from her family and established what her DNA sample would have looked like. The tests showed that the blood on the clothing and in the pub had come from a child of the McCourt family. It appeared to be the final nail in Ian Simmons case.

Ian Simms' passage to court, a year or so after the murder, was far from smooth. There had already been angry demonstrations outside the George and Dragon and the tabloids had taken great interest in the case, helping to stir up passions.

The final piece in the prosecution case, a motive, was unveiled at the trial. It was revealed that Helen's diary mentioned Simms' name and that he'd been overheard saying he hated her. Furthermore, Helen had been in a bust-up with another girl in the bar a few nights before she disappeared and the pair had been put out of the establishment. The Crown contended that Helen had gone into the closed pub on her way home to make sure she wasn't barred for any reason. Somehow a fight had developed and Simms had killed her. A witness claimed she'd heard a scream coming from the George and Dragon the night Helen disappeared.

However, the defence made some telling points. The butterfly clip didn't fit Helen's earring at all. Nor had the earring been handmade for Helen. It came from Ratner's, the cut-price high street jewellery store, which would eventually suffer a devastating slump in trade when its chairman claimed his products were 'crap'. At the time, there were thousands of earrings exactly like it being worn by women all over Britain. There were also problems with what was claimed to be the murder weapon – the extension cable that Ian Simms had so readily identified while he was in police custody. Because of its strange shape, nobody, apparently, could work out how it could be used to strangle someone. And there was more. Witnesses told of how Helen would drape her coat over the bar stool when she sat in the pub, presumably putting it in contact with the floor where someone could have stood on it. Tears in her coat, which, the Crown had claimed were proof of a struggle, turned out to be not as damning as they had originally appeared. Witnesses testified they'd noticed them as she travelled on her last bus journey home before she disappeared. As for the scratches on Ian Simms' body, a forensic pathologist, from the Royal Albert Edward Hospital in Wigan, testified that they did not suggest that a young woman fighting for her life had inflicted them.

And there was also the strange way that Simms had handled the aftermath of the murder. If he'd managed to hide the young woman's body so successfully that it hadn't been found, why did he leave so much incriminating evidence – the clothes, the bag – lying around? And why did he so readily admit to the police that the jacket was his and the flex came from his pub?

The thrust of Simms' defence seemed to hang on the fact that there was a month between his arrest and the discovery of much of the most damning forensic evidence. During that time, the pub was closed and unoccupied. Anyone could have gone in and planted evidence there. Had he been framed? However, there was still the DNA evidence. And it was apparently strong. The blood found on the Labatt's sweatshirt had been matched to the blood given by the McCourts. It was, the experts concluded, 28,000 times more likely to have come from a member of the McCourt family than any other member of the public.

The jury was convinced and Ian Simms was convicted of the murder of Helen McCourt on 14 March 1989.

The case was viewed as yet another success story for DNA profiling. It was the first trial in which a murderer had been convicted on its forensic application. But, in the general murmur of approval that greeted the verdict, that very low statistical certainty given by the DNA experts went largely ignored. In the space of a year or so, DNA evidence had dropped from a certainty of millions, even billions to one to just 16,000 to one.

The reason for that slump was the change in technique. Alec Jeffreys had done the groundwork – and what groundwork it was – but the real battle was just beginning. Compromises were already being made in the struggle to transform DNA fingerprinting into a universal crime-fighting tool. The first thing to be sacrificed was the high discriminating power – those billions to one statistics. When it came to the sort of highly degraded samples found at crime scenes, the choice was between testing them with single-locus probes, with their higher sensitivity and lower discriminating power, or not testing them at all. DNA fingerprinting, with its multi-locus probes, didn't work at those levels.

Nobody had abandoned the desire to have foolproof results. In fact, the race was on to find what would become the holy trinity of DNA profiling – tests with high sensitivity, high discriminating power and the ability to be completed quickly. These were a long way away. It was still taking up to four weeks to produce a single DNA profile.

The process was extremely labour intensive and the results were hard to decipher without a great deal of knowledge. Most frustratingly, the actual work involved in preparing a DNA profile only took about four days. The rest of the time was spent waiting for chemical reactions to take place and for radioactive photographs to develop.

The DNA evidence in the Ian Simms case was to be questioned many years later when his case was taken up by those campaigning against miscarriages of justice. One respected investigative journalist, Bob Woffinden, intrigued by the inconsistencies in the case and the lack of a body or motive, wrote a lengthy article in *The Guardian* re-examining the evidence. Simms had had a hard time in prison, he noted. He had been vilified by the tabloids and, as a result, had been beaten up on a number of occasions by fellow prisoners. His wife had divorced him and remarried. Yet he had consistently proclaimed his innocence. In his *Guardian* piece, Woffinden drew attention to the DNA evidence and questioned whether it was significantly strong enough to have turned the case. He noted that Dr Alec Jeffreys had made a cameo appearance in court, which seemed to have had a tremendous impact on the judge who appeared dazzled by the great scientist's aura. Woffinden's campaign was firmly met by Helen McCourt's mother, Marie, who had also campaigned for years after the case. She wanted Simms prosecuted for not revealing the whereabouts of her daughter's body.

No serious dents were made in Simms' conviction but there was a curious consequence of the journalist's intervention. After considering the *Guardian* article, the Home Office's reaction was not to review the case but to ban journalists from visiting prisoners unless they agreed beforehand not to write about their conversations. Those who said the new ruling would prevent miscarriages of justice ever being exposed greeted this draconian measure with horror. It was eventually appealed to the House of Lords. When the ruling was overturned, it ended a small, but shabby, episode in British legal history.

There was now worldwide attention being focused on the forensic breakthroughs taking place in England. The Federal Bureau of Investigation assigned a team to investigate the new techniques and report back on their usefulness. At the same time, the US government set their own staff the task of looking into the possibility of coming up with an American test. The FBI was not going to rush into anything though. James Kerney, a forensic scientist with the bureau, was quoted in 1986 as saying that, although he was impressed with what he had seen,

DNA profiling was a long way off. He said it would take 'between two to five years' to refine it for standard use and warned that introducing it prematurely could damage its credibility.

The Americans had another problem. All new technologies used in court cases have to comply with the Kelly Frye standard which states they must first have been accepted as trustworthy and reliable by the scientific community before they are accepted as admissible evidence in court. DNA testing was so new it hadn't even been seen, let alone tried, by most of the scientific community.

Not surprisingly, perhaps, given the Americans' interest in the technology, the next big breakthrough would come about as a result of something discovered across the Atlantic. In fact, the discovery had been made long before Dr Alec Jeffreys had stumbled across DNA fingerprinting. It had just taken a while to filter through.

The side of a sun-dappled highway in Mendocino County, California, would seem an unlikely place for a chemist to make a scientific discovery that would result in him being awarded the Nobel Prize for Chemistry but that's where Dr Kary Mullis says it happened. Mullis, as quintessentially American as Alec Jeffreys is British, was driving his beaten-up Honda car towards the Anderson Valley where he had a cabin. It was May 1983. His girlfriend, Nancy, was asleep in the seat beside him, evening was falling and it had been a very hot day. As he drove, Kary Mullis was daydreaming about chemicals, DNA, the difficulties of getting big enough samples to work on and the different things he could cook up to get around the problem. Off the top of his head, he conjured up an image of a series of chemical procedures that would multiply DNA in such a way as to make millions and millions of copies. It would give limitless supplies of source material for everyone to work on. He was just playing around but the more he thought of the chemical steps he had come up with, the more he realised that it could probably be done. All the phases in the multiplication sequence he envisaged had been tried separately and were established scientific techniques – they'd just never been put together before. He told his girlfriend he'd just thought of something 'incredible'. She slept on. Bubbling with excitement now he pulled the car over. He was at mile marker 46.58 on Highway 128, he would later remember. With a pencil he started scribbling part of his idea down. The lead broke. No matter.

He had already confirmed that, if his technique worked, the order of magnitude by which DNA samples would multiply was enormous. Every cycle of his new test would yield a major increase. If he did ten cycles it would be 1024, twenty cycles would give a million and thirty, a billion. By the time he got to his cabin in the hills, Dr Kary Mullis was beside himself with excitement. He spent the whole evening and most of the night scribbling down the blueprint for a technique that would make such vast numbers of copies of any DNA sequence in the world. Everybody would want to use it. He told himself he would be famous. He told himself he would win the Nobel Prize.

A few days later, Kary Mullis came back down to the earth with a bump. He asked himself why, if his technique was so simple, no one else had ever tried it before. But he didn't walk away from it. Instead, he keyed the details into a file on his computer. This was where he put all his great ideas. Then he searched the literature to see if it had been tried before. He could find no trace of it. He phoned colleagues and asked them if they had ever heard of it. He drew a blank. Then he started asking people if there was any reason they thought it wouldn't work. Nobody could think of one. The thing that surprised him the most was that nobody seemed nearly as excited about his idea as he was.

Perhaps that wasn't really too surprising. Kary Mullis was no ordinary scientist. When he won his Nobel Prize, many years later, the press had to tour California's beaches to try to find him. He'd gone surfing. When he went to Sweden for the glittering award ceremony, he took his former wife, his new girlfriend and his son – although, funnily enough, so did the only other scientist winning a Nobel Prize for Chemistry that year. When he would later go on television to talk about his breakthrough, everybody was worried he'd talk, instead, about the fun he'd had taking LSD. He did.

Krazy Kary, as he would later be known, had an apparently idyllic childhood in South Carolina. In his brilliant autobiography, *Dancing Naked in the Mind Field* (New York: Pantheon Books, 1998), he recounts how his mother would allow him to choose his Christmas presents from home delivery catalogues. One year he selected a Gilbert chemistry set. He augmented it with chemicals bought from the local drugstore and, on occasion, with explosive fuses he got from the hardware store.

At the age of seven, he succeeded in setting a very large tree alight after one experiment went wrong.

The chemistry bug had bitten and, when Kary Mullis graduated from high school, he got a summer job at a local chemical supply firm, Columbia Organic. His popularity with the boss soared when he discovered how one of their suppliers, a company called Fluka, was making a nice killing from them. Every time someone asked for a particular chemical from Columbia Organic, they would order it from Fluka at $100-a-gramme. What nobody at Columbia had noticed was that they had the very same chemical in stock under a different name. Fluka would just order it right back from Columbia at $24-a-gramme and send it straight on to Columbia's customer.

Mullis went to Georgia Tech to study biochemistry but that wasn't enough for him. Noticing that the rare chemicals Columbia needed were hard to get hold of and expensive, he started a sideline manufacturing his own chemicals in a friend's garage. It brought predictable results, which included covering his friend's neighbourhood in a noxious gas cloud, resulting in the death of an azalea bush. He also set fire to the drains and sewers at Georgia Tech when he rather carelessly dumped a batch of chemicals down them. Mullis was a star before he was a star. By the time he had graduated and started working in research, he was already well known for his boundless enthusiasm and his relaxed attitude to the tiresome rules of life.

It may have been that attitude which prompted his colleagues to take his ideas about DNA multiplication with a pinch of salt. The world wasn't changed in a day and Kary was always thinking out of the box. He did drag his heels a bit. In fact, it took until that September before he actually got around to setting up an experiment to test his new theory. Naturally, he wasn't going to do anything quietly so he came up with a scheme that, he thought, would shock the scientific world.

A company called Genetech had just cloned a 400 nucleotide (i.e., large) DNA fragment from human nerve growth factor. They had published details of their sensational breakthrough in *Nature*. Kary Mullis decided he would make his own 400-nucleotide fragment using polymerase chain reaction (PCR), as he was to call his technique for rapidly producing many copies of a fragment of DNA. Instead of the process taking months, as it had done at Genetech, he would do it almost overnight. He set up an experiment in his lab at the biotech company, Cetus. He placed human DNA and nerve growth factor in a screw-cap tube 'with an O-ring and a purple top', as he would say in his memoirs. He boiled it, cooled it, added the DNA polymerase, set it to maintain exactly 37 degrees and then went home for the evening. When he returned the next day he made a significant discovery. It didn't work.

Bowed but not broken, Mullis re-examined his theory. He realised that, although it was sound, it would be better to start with a simpler piece of DNA material and better still to conduct the experiment by hand – even if this meant he would have to carry out the tedious process of mixing in the ingredients himself. He was right. On the night of 16 December 1983, after his next experiment, he developed a piece of radioactive film and saw, on the negative, a tiny little black band. It meant, as he recalls in his book, he 'was going to be famous'.

It took almost exactly ten years for his Nobel Prize to be awarded. The delay, his colleagues said, was because he was too controversial, too outspoken for the Nobel Committee's taste. They were taking their time so that he would mature a little – cool down. They eventually realised they were wasting their time. Dr Kary Mullis stopped off at the White House to meet the Clintons on the way to the prize ceremony in Sweden. He grilled Hillary Clinton on world health policy and pronounced himself impressed with her responses. In Sweden, he offered his sixteen-year-old son in marriage to the daughter of the King and Queen of Sweden. They laughed. He was almost arrested at his hotel for shining a laser pen at passers-by. Not a smart move in what, at that time, was understandably assassination-jittery Sweden. But the world loved him. Pictures of the crazy scientist and his surfboard adorned the front pages of newspapers around the globe.

While the Nobel Committee had been dragging its feet, the rest of the world of science hadn't. It had taken a while, naturally, for the word to spread about what PCR could do but then it just sort of took off. Cetus sold the rights to Hoffman Laroche for $300m. Not much of that money came Dr Mullis's way, he would later grumble.

It hadn't escaped the notice of the forensic scientists that here was a way to solve one of the major problems with DNA profiling. By using

PCR, tiny fragments of DNA could be enormously increased in size, prior to being tested. No longer would they have to struggle to find large chunks of useable material. PCR was a genetic photocopier. Put in a fragment at one end and thousands of copies would come flying out the other. It seemed to be tailor-made for the process.

The first opportunity to try it out came in England, of course – a country that was by now streaking ahead of everybody else in its seemingly boundless enthusiasm for the new science. Unlike the Helen McCourt case, the next murder would be all about a person that nobody cared about – a young woman who was so alone in the world that, when she disappeared, not a single person seemed to notice.

The case of 'The Body Under The Patio' would become a nationwide obsession in Britain in the early '90s. It wasn't a real-life killing but one of the most captivating storylines of Merseyside-set soap, *Brookside*. What most of the viewers didn't realise, as they shared every twist and turn in Mandy Jordache's desperate struggle to stop her abusive husband Trevor's remains from being found, was that the whole thing was loosely based on a real-life story. A tragic real-life story.

On 7 December 1989, at 4 p.m. to be exact, builders, working on the garden of a terraced house that was divided into a number of flats, at Fitzhamon Embankment, Cardiff, discovered a rolled up carpet tied with cable. When they opened it they found a black plastic bin bag inside and, inside that, they found what looked like a human skeleton. It was grisly find. The flesh had gone from the body but there were lustrous blonde curls on the skull that had somehow survived. When the police arrived to take a closer look, they found what they later described as no more than a 'bag of bones'. But there was no doubt foul play had taken place. Electrical cord could be seen binding the wrists of the victim behind its back. A crime had taken place. A murder most probably. But nobody had the faintest idea who the victim was.

The young victim then got the sort of attention that she had never had during her short, harsh life. Experts from all over England were mobilised to try to help piece together some way of identifying the skeleton. The remains embarked on an extraordinary journey as, step by step, the veil was removed from her life and a ladder was extended into her past.

The first thing to do – and it's always the first thing in these sort of cases – is to establish the age, height and sex of the victim. David Whittaker, a dental anatomist at Heath Hospital, Cardiff, was asked to examine the skull. He noted that the wisdom teeth had not yet grown through, that the second molar teeth were present and had been established (they are not normally fully developed until about age fifteen) and that the roots of the third molar teeth were in the early stages of development. He estimated the victim's age was around fifteen and a half.

Meanwhile, forensic entomologist, Doctor Zakaria Erzinclioglu of Cambridge University, was studying parts of the remains and some soil taken from around the grave to try to work out when the murder had taken place. His speciality was the life cycles of insects – insects that would settle on a corpse at different stages in its decay. It was and is a crucially important method of estimating how long a body has lain in the ground. The details weren't pretty but they were fascinating. He found a well-established colony of breeding woodlice and signs that coffin flies, which live on decaying flesh, had been there. He reckoned it would have taken three years for the coffin flies to consume the body and another two years for the woodlice to build a colony around fungus, which grew on the bone. Woodlice and phorid flies, a species of coffin fly, don't like to live together so the doctor estimated the body must have been in the ground for at least five years. In his examination, Dr Erzinclioglu also noticed around ten larval cases, which would have been left behind when bluebottle pupae turned into adult flies. They are normally laid above ground and couldn't have penetrated the soil the body was buried in so the doctor suspected it had not been buried immediately after death. He was to prove to be spot on.

A picture was slowly beginning to emerge but it was still very patchy. Many more details were needed. The next stopping point on the journey was London's Natural History Museum. The remains arrived in a cardboard box, carried by a plain-clothes detective. They were handed over to the care of Chris Stringer, Rob Krusynski and Theya Molleson, all members of the museum's Human Origins Group and all experts in cranial, or skull, reconstruction.

They took thirty-three different measurements from the skull, fed them into a computer program called CRANID, or cranial identification, and waited for the results. It compared their measurements to more than 2,500 taken from sixty different groups of people worldwide. It took only a couple of minutes to flash up the result. The skull, it predicted, belonged to a Caucasian female of mixed British and non-British parentage. Her larger teeth, in particular, indicated the non-British parent was possibly of eastern European origin.

The next person to come into this daisy chain of experts was Richard Neave, a medical artist at Manchester University. Mr Neave was an expert at reconstructing facial tissue, fleshing out bones and bringing the features of the long dead back to life. He made a model of the skull and then started to add layers of clay, millimetre by millimetre, to represent flesh and skin. Finally, hair, nose and eyes were added to give a life-like impression of what the young girl would have looked like before she died. It was an extremely impressive result. The police now had a real missing person to try to trace rather than a featureless skeleton.

They photographed the model and had posters made up. The posters were distributed to police stations across the country, reproduced in newspapers and even shown on television. The blitz worked. Within two days, two social workers had come forward to say they thought the girl in the posters resembled Karen Price, a youngster who had run away from council care in 1981.

It appeared that Karen Price was never missed by anybody in her life. At the age of ten, she had been taken into care when her parents Michael Price and Anita Nicholaidas – who was, as the CRANID program had predicted, of Greek Cypriot extraction – divorced. After years in care, she ran away from an assessment centre in Pontypridd on 8 May 1981, not long before her sixteenth birthday. Karen had been sent there for advice on her future now that she was nearing the age when she could strike out on her own. Her disappearance was reported to the police but she was a runaway, nearly sixteen, and nobody bothered much about it.

The police now had a victim and they had a pretty strong clue that she must have been killed at the flat at Fitzhamon Embankment. The same carpet that had been used to wrap her body had also been used to cover its floor. It was also the only flat that had access to the garden. However, it wasn't that easy. In the eight years between Karen running away and her body being found, 700 people had lived in the Victorian terraced property. The police turned to the BBC's *Crimewatch UK* programme and made a public appeal for information.

It was watched by one Idris Ali who was stunned to see a face from the past – a face he had thought he would never see again – staring back at him from the television screen. He told his friends he had been to school with Karen. His friends told the police. During questioning, Ali broke down and confessed to having seen the killing of Karen Price. He told them of another man, Alan Charlton, who had recently served a prison sentence for the attempted rape of a fifty-five-year-old woman. Ali also named a thirteen-year-old girl he said had been present in the flat when Karen was killed.

A sad story of the young girl's final days then emerged. When he was just sixteen, Ali had befriended Karen at the assessment centre and urged her to run away. On the streets, he managed to persuade her to turn to prostitution to get money for both of them. Along the way, he picked up the thirteen-year-old girl and became her pimp too. Sometime later, he met Charlton at a party. That's where Charlton, a thirty-one-year-old roofer, suggested the two of them could team up and make some money. He would organise drugs and pornographic movie parties in his flat and the girls could procure clients. Ali agreed.

In July 1981, the four of them were in the garden flat when Charlton suggested he take some nude photos of the girls. The girls refused. In front of the others, Charlton beat Karen to death. Four days later, he and Ali buried her body in the back garden. When, following Ali's evidence, the thirteen-year-old girl was traced, she agreed to give evidence against Charlton. All the pieces in the jigsaw seemed to have fallen into place and Karen Price was finally going to get some justice.

There was, however, a problem that was worrying the police and the Crown Office. Another expert, Peter Vanezis, the head of forensic medicine at Charing Cross and Westminster Medical School in London, had superimposed photos of Karen on to photos of the skull that had been discovered in the garden. There was a match. But it wasn't that strong. It simply showed there was nothing in the skull that would rule out the possibility of it being Karen's. Karen's dental records had also been pulled and these seemed to match. However, these were not seen as offering strong enough evidence to guarantee that the body had been identified and so secure a murder conviction. The defence would surely attack the reconstruction on the basis that it was not scientific enough, not accurate enough, to prove conclusively that it was Karen's body.

The police then turned to Alec Jeffreys. He agreed to help but immediately saw that they faced the problem of extracting enough useable DNA from the body. Dr Erica Hagelberg, a biochemist at Oxford University, was given that task. She sandblasted a section of bone to clean it and then took a tiny of sample of DNA from it. She discovered that there was human DNA present but only a tiny amount. The remaining 99 per cent came from the fungus and bacteria that had invaded the corpse. There was nowhere near enough to produce a proper DNA profile. If that had happened a year or so earlier, it would have been the end of the story. But Dr Hagelberg took the tiny human DNA fragment and subjected it to Kary Mullis's PCR technique. It greatly multiplied the sample, producing ample qualities for Jeffreys to work on.

Nothing in life is simple and there was another difficulty. The kind of DNA produced by PCR does not lend itself to the same type of tests as fresh DNA. Normally, the regions of DNA Jeffreys would select for examination would be between 1,000 and 10,000 units long. The PCR technique produced much shorter regions. Undaunted, Dr Jeffreys selected a set of six new smaller regions for comparison and carried out what was essentially a new test. Again it worked. By comparing the DNA from Karen with DNA from both her parents, he was able to say, with 99.9 per cent certainty, that it was her body.

Karen Price's murder trial broke new ground in British criminal history. Three new forensic techniques were used – PCR, the use of DNA extracted from bone and Jeffreys' technique of using small regions of DNA for comparison. The defence attacked the new techniques but it made little difference. Alan Charlton was sentenced to life imprisonment on 26 February 1991.

After the trial, Detective Superintendent Neale Evans, deputy head of CID at South Wales Police, said the DNA evidence had been extremely important. 'We wanted to charge a man with murder,' he said. 'So we had to be sure of the girl's identity. We weren't totally happy with what we had because we felt there was a need to positively establish identity by other methods.'

DNA

For young Karen Price, the verdict signalled the end of an extra-ordinary journey. In death she had been paid so much more attention than she ever was in life. Her remains had travelled around the country to be picked over and prodded and her features had been beamed into the homes of millions of people as the search for her killer took place. It was undignified but it was justifiable. She was finally laid to rest in a decent grave during a small ceremony, which was attended, in a fitting sort of way, by representatives from the police.

5

FIGHTBACK

It is 27 April 1994, Jarrett, Virginia, USA. The clock on the wall indicates that it is approaching 11 p.m. Timothy W Spencer is seated and leather straps are tied across his chest, thighs, legs and arms. A prison officer leans down and attaches a copper electrode to his leg, at a point that has already been shaved bare. A metal helmet containing a wet sponge is strapped to the top of his head, also shaved. It is now after 11 p.m. A man named Ellis B Wright Jr, the warden of the Greensville Correction Center, leans forward and asks Mr Spencer if he has any last words. 'Oh, yeah, I think so,' Mr Spencer replies. He then falls silent, his eyes casting around the room drinking in the scene. Everybody watches him. Is he thinking about thirty-five-year-old Debbie Davis, who was raped and strangled in her Virginia apartment on 17 September 1987? Or perhaps of thirty-two-year-old surgeon, Susan Hellams, whose dead body was found in a cupboard in her home by her husband? Or even of fifteen-year-old Diane Cho, yet another victim, who was found in a cupboard of her home? Or perhaps his memories of the final victim, forty-four-year-old Susan Tucker, who lay dead in her flat for a week after she was strangled, have come flooding back? Possibly he is cursing himself for tidying the flats after he raped and murdered the women. It was a pretty stupid thing to do considering the police knew his style was to break into houses when the victims were sleeping and clean up before he left. However, it is unlikely the women cross his mind at all. Right up until now, Timothy W Spencer has shown no remorse for his victims or their families. It would be surprising if he suddenly blurted out an apology or even a confession. There was no sign of it as he waited in the death cell a few minutes ago. All he had had to say was that he didn't want his organs going to medical research or even for transplant purposes. The seconds tick by as Spencer's eyes gaze around the room. Could he be thinking

75

the same thoughts as the warden and the prison staff? Hoping, maybe, that he doesn't go the same way as Wilbert Lee Evans who had sat in this very chair – the original Old Sparky, which was built using convict labour in the '60s – a few years ago. According to the word in the prison, blood had spewed out of the right side of Wilbert's mask the second the electricity was applied. It had poured down the front of his shirt, making a sizzling sound as it dripped from his lips. Of course, Timothy had known Wilbert. He had known Derrick Lynn Peterson too. Derrick had gone to the chair three years before and, as everyone in the room knew, they'd botched that execution as well. It took seven and a half minutes of shocks, with pauses while Dr David Barnes leant over to check the pulse, before he died. Still, Virginia was improving. In 1982, when Frank Coppola had been electrocuted, his head and leg had caught fire and smoke had filled the execution chamber.

Tonight, though, they weren't going to mess about. Timothy knew that. They'd changed the system. More shocks. Fewer checks. Well, no professional checks. The doctor had refused to take part in the process – something about medical ethics. Maybe it won't be that bad. Timothy W Spencer has probably heard of Willie Francis, the seventeen-year-old who survived the electric chair in 1946. Willie had later said, 'My mouth tasted like cold peanut butter. I felt a burning in my head and left leg and I jumped against the straps.' Of course, they took Willie back and fried him the next year. Ha! You don't escape justice that easily.

Timothy also probably knows that the first shock of 2000 volts is supposed to cook the brain and kill the central nervous system. Every muscle in the body, including the heart, contracts and stays contracted while the current is applied for a minute or so. True, eyeballs sometimes pop out, the body turns bright red and the skin swells to bursting point. There's often smoke, sometimes flames, especially if the prisoner is a sweaty type, and usually gurgling, foaming and bleeding through the skin. But, as Timothy has no doubt been told, the prisoner is supposed to be rendered unconscious in 0.0042 of a second. Timothy's eyes come back into focus. A whole twenty seconds have now elapsed since he last said a word – a whole twenty seconds of silence. He turns towards the warden. Is he going to say something? No. He looks up at Ellis B Wright Jr and just nods. Two prison officers move forward and attach a leather mask to his face, tightening the straps at the back of his head, covering most of his features. The signal is given for the executioner to flip the switch. Timothy W Spencer is about to make history for the second time in his relatively short, horrifically violent life. There is no botch up. Timothy W Spencer, the Southside Strangler, clenches as the first of four shocks courses through his body. He is supposed to. That's it. He is dead. The clock above his head reads 11.13 p.m. It is barely half an hour since the United States Supreme Court refused his request to have his DNA samples retested. It is barely twenty-five minutes since he was told that he'd reached the end of that road.

Of course, Timothy knew all about DNA testing. He has lived with its consequences on Death Row for six years. In July 1988, he became the first person in the USA to be convicted of murder using the revolutionary new technique. Semen samples, taken from the bodies of Susan Tucker, Susan Hellams and Debbie Davis, had been tested and all of them matched his. There was a one in 135 million chance they'd got the wrong man, the court was told. That was the first time he'd made history. The second time was tonight when he died. Then Timothy W Spencer became the first person in the world to be executed on the basis of DNA evidence.

How did it happen so fast? In the mid '80s, the FBI had said they had grave doubts about the readiness of DNA testing. It was still years away from being introduced in the United States the Bureau had insisted. They'd been over to England and they'd looked at Alex Jeffreys' discovery. Of course, they hadn't taken into account the fact that every police force in the USA naturally wanted to take their own look at this new wonder tool. And they weren't going to sit around and wait. No Siree! Not when the tests were already available commercially. With or without the FBI's seal of approval, and who needed it, DNA testing hit the ground running in the USA. After all, there was money to be made and crimes to be solved. Florida was the first state to use the tests to get a conviction. When Tommy Lee Andrews was arrested for carrying out a string of rapes, the police were only able to get enough evidence to convict him on two of them. After he was sent to prison for twenty-two years, an assistant state attorney, Tim Berry, read about Jeffreys' discovery in England and how some US companies were looking at it.

He got in touch with the Lifecodes Corporation in New York to ask if they could run tests on semen samples taken from the other rapes in the Tommy Lee Andrews case. The ones they hadn't got a conviction on. They matched and Tommy Lee Andrews got another sixty-five years in prison to add to the twenty-two he was already enjoying. Flushed with success, Michael Baird, a senior figure in the Lifecodes Corporation, announced, 'If you're a criminal, it's like leaving your name, address and social security number at the scene of the crime.' It was 1988. DNA fingerprinting had arrived big time in the states.

On 22 September that year, Timothy W Spencer was convicted of the murders of two of his victims and the death sentence was passed. Lifecodes' phones were ringing off the hook as prosecutors all over the US suddenly wanted to try this new wonder technique. Things were moving with incredible speed. But the FBI had been right. It was all coming a bit too thick and fast. The nation's defence lawyers were caught with their pants well and truly down. Mostly they were totally bamboozled by this infallible new technology. Mostly they couldn't do anything to challenge it. But, as is always the case, there were exceptions. Two New York lawyers were about to poke a stick into the wheels of justice. They would refuse to be intimidated by the technology and start the first fight back against its so-called infallibility. Eventually they would light a beacon that would be seen all over the country. In just over a year, DNA testing would be seen in an altogether different light. But that's getting ahead of the game. Back in 1988, the two questions no lawyers ever seemed to ask were – 'How does DNA testing work?' and 'How do you disprove it?'

The answer to the first question was pretty straightforward. Broken down into its key steps, DNA fingerprinting was surprisingly dull and unexotic. What Alec Jeffreys actually discovered and named DNA fingerprinting was based on a technique known as Restriction Fragment Length Polymorphism. What it is, in layman's terms, is a way to compare the lengths and patterns of different fragments of DNA. That's it. These fragments didn't hold the secrets of life or even the more mundane characteristics that mark people out as individuals in life. In fact, the bits Professor Jeffreys selected, the stuttering bits, contain no information about their donor at all. They are what is known as junk DNA. They're leftover scraps of DNA, which have been tossed from the genetic workbench and left to lie in the dusty corners of the human genome. They are only of interest because they occur in well-known spots on the chromosome and, of course, they're pretty unique to every individual.

So all the tests do is seek out the stuttered bits, sort them into lengths and stick the donor's name on them. A person's DNA profile is simply a set of numbers, nothing more, nothing less. It doesn't mean that that person has black hair or a big nose or even blue eyes. It means that one particular pattern of black bands on an x-ray film, which corresponds to the lengths of these fragments, can be found in certain areas of their DNA. It gets even more mundane. There is no such thing as an absolutely individual DNA profile and there probably never will be. Think of a bank account number. Everyone's bank account number is different but, when the teller punches it into his or her computer the right name appears on the screen. The numbers themselves don't mean anything. They're not codes for whether that person has an overdraft, never pays their bills or even whether that person is the bank manager's wife and, therefore, should be given top priority treatment. They're just numbers that don't contain any information at all except for the identity of one person. That's what a DNA profile is.

There's a reason for this. Human beings have twenty-three pairs of chromosomes, twenty-two from the father, twenty-two from the mother plus two, the x and y chromosomes, which denote sex. Inside each chromosome are four parts, represented by the chemical letters A (adenine), T (thymine), G (guanine) and C (cytosine). It took until 1999 to map out just one of these chromosomes. It was Chromosome Number 22. Number 22 was selected to be the first to be mapped out not because researchers suspected it could perhaps hold the meaning of life but because it was the shortest. It contained a mere twenty-three million chemical letters. After it had been unlocked and when the champagne corks had stopped popping and the party streamers were taken down, everyone started to get down to the real task – working out what the letter sequence they'd uncovered in Chromosome 22 actually meant.

To have an absolutely individual DNA profile – one that would allow a forensic scientist to stand up in court and say, 'Based on the DNA evidence, I can guarantee that is the man there.' – all twenty-three chromosomes, with their average of thirty million letters each, would have to be profiled. It isn't going to happen. It doesn't need to happen. There is enough variety in the junk DNA sections to allow staggeringly high odds against a false match to be worked out. In fact, only a handful of points, or alleles, of human DNA are examined. In the early days, it was often just four. How scientists came up with the staggeringly high odds that someone would have the same pattern is dead easy. They just worked out the chances of each particular allele appearing in another human being. So, say allele 1 occurs in twenty per cent of the population and allele 2 occurs in five per cent of the population, the odds of one in five and one in twenty are multiplied together to give one in a hundred. Then the other two alleles' odds are thrown into the pot and you end up with big multipliers.

The actual scientific process of preparing a DNA profile was time consuming and complex but not too hard to understand. It had eight separate stages and went something like this. A piece of DNA is extracted in the lab. There are roughly ten trillion cells in the human body and all of them, except red blood cells, contain DNA so it is not exactly difficult to find. The first thing the technicians do is give it the once over to check that it hasn't been lying around too long and 'gone off'. This is science so there ain't no sell-by date on DNA material. Instead, they weigh it to check that there are still enough molecules in it for its expected size. It's called a high molecular count to weight. The next step is to turn this DNA sample into the sort of fragments that the Jeffreys test compares. This is done by rounding them up into the right groups and getting rid of the unwanted ones. That's pretty straightforward. Biological scissors, called restriction enzymes, are set among the DNA like a bunch of microscopic sheepdogs. They recognise the different DNA bits and cut it at specific points. When they're finished, they've got all the pieces they want – around a million fragments – in one big blob. Incidentally, it is crucially important that the enzymes are given enough time to round up or digest everything. If that isn't done, then there are spare bits left over and the results go haywire.

Anyway, this blob of DNA fragments is dunked into something called an agarose gel where the pieces are zapped into their different sizes during a process called electrophoresis. To get down to the nitty-gritty, and separate out the fragment lengths that the scientists want, a process called Southern Blot Hybridisation, named after its inventor, a Dr Southern, is then called into play. The blot part refers to blotting the DNA from the gel on to a nylon membrane to which the radioactive hybridisation probes are added.

Once everything is switched to a membrane filter, more radioactivity is called on to help the target fragments finally show up. It is the different lengths of these fragments that give us the DNA profiles. Lengths of bits of DNA – that's what a profile is.

The technique that Alec Jeffreys had pioneered when he invented DNA fingerprinting was known as a multi-locus probe. This probe was radioactive and acted like a single magnet sticking to fragments from a large number of different DNA locations. It gave the big blocky pictures like the one Professor Jeffreys has on his wall at Leicester University.

By the time the Americans came on the scene, everyone had switched to using several single-locus probes – as had been done in the Tommy Lee Andrews case. The reason for this was due to the fact that, because there was so much information available from Jeffreys' probe – the original and technically the only method of DNA fingerprinting – you need someone with a lot of experience and expertise to pronounce a match. Instead of just randomly sucking up huge sections of DNA, each single-locus probe targets a specific region of the junk DNA and pulls out the fragments from its own particular site. The advantage of this was it gave pictures with less banding and this meant they were much easier to interpret.

Irrespective of which probe is used, the pattern in the fragments is then turned into something that can be seen by the naked eye by exposing it on an x-ray film. With multi-locus probes, the pattern is wide and would cover the whole of a sheet of A4 paper. With the later single-locus probes, just two bands are produced – one from the father and one from the mother. And that was pretty much the state of the DNA science in the United States in August 1989 when a trial took place that would change the course of DNA profiling for years to come.

It had all started on a cold February afternoon in the Bronx. David Rivera was locked out of his flat. He was sure his pregnant partner,

Vilma Ponce, and their two-year-old daughter, Natasha, were in but, for some reason, they weren't answering the door. David had gone to the call box in the grocery store and phoned. No answer. Was she asleep? He didn't know. He phoned his mother just to check in case Vilma had gone out unexpectedly. 'Nope,' said his mother, she'd spoken to Vilma not long before and they'd discussed what she was going to cook for dinner. She was surely in. Now, getting concerned, he asked his mother to call the police and get them to send someone around. He stood outside the apartment in the street and whistled up at the window. As he waited with his fingers in his mouth, a man came out the apartment building. He was covered in blood. David stared at him. The man smiled and walked by him to cross the street. David rushed upstairs and forced his way into the apartment. The whole place was covered in blood. Vilma Ponce had been stabbed fifty-eight times, little Natasha sixteen times. The police found a brown paper bag in the flat containing fresh chicken and steak. The meal Vilma had been planning to make that night.

A couple of days later, Rivera returned to the flat, accompanied by police officers, to get some of his stuff from it. As he was leaving and just as the police drove off, he saw the man who had walked out of the building the day Vilma died. He went over and asked him to smile. The man did. It was the same guy. Rivera went straight down to the 48th Precinct and told the police. They got the mug shot books out and he picked out one Joseph Castro. Right from the start it looked like Castro. Vilma's friend, Barbara Troy, it transpired, had spotted Castro, a few days earlier when the two women were out together. Vilma had told Barbara that the guy had tried to hit on her even though she was pregnant. Then the police discovered that Castro, an assistant school janitor, had actually been in Vilma Ponce's apartment to repair a lock a few weeks before.

While Joseph Castro was being interviewed in the Bronx Police Station, a detective had noticed a brown mark on his watchstrap that looked like a bloodstain. He took the watch to his boss. Risa Sugarman, thirty-four, chief of the Bronx District Attorneys Homicide Department, and ordered every blood test going to be carried out on it. The police wanted to be sure. The problem was that Vilma Ponce's partner, David Rivera, it was said, had a history of beating Vilma. The police were concerned that Castro's defence would have been founded on the claim that Rivera had done the murder and engineered the crime scene to make it look like Castro was guilty.

To Risa Sugarman, 'every blood test going' meant trying the new technique of DNA profiling which was available from the private Lifecodes Corporation, based in Valhalla, New York. Just over five months after the murder, Lifecodes' report on the Castro watchstrap came in to Sugarman's office. It said there was a perfect match between Vilma Ponce's blood and the bloodstain found on the watchstrap. The odds against it being someone else's blood, the corporation said, were 198,000,000-to-one. Bingo. Castro was their man.

The problem, as assistant district attorney Sugarman knew, was that there was no way any New York court, let alone a Bronx court, was going to allow this newfangled DNA technology to be used in a complex murder trial without a lot of legal examination to discover whether it was any good or not. He was right.

The fundamental question that the judge in the Castro case wanted answered was 'Did DNA testing meet the Frye Standard?'. The Frye Standard, or the Frye Test, had been introduced in 1923 to weed out the crackpot from the genuine in so-called scientific tests. And there had been a lot of crackpot tests going around. Basically, the new technique had to have been accepted by, and be in general use within, the scientific community before it could be used in court. By the time the Castro case came to court, in the autumn of 1988, it looked like the argument was half won. Justice had passed Castro by and three courts in the state, and many outside it, had already allowed DNA evidence. It had also been accepted in Timothy W Spencer's case in Virginia, in July of that year, but that didn't figure in any Bronx courts' deliberations. Anyway, the point was DNA testing looked like it was pretty sound. One judge had gone so far as to pronounce that DNA testing was 'incapable of giving a wrong answer'. Except it wasn't – as a shocked world was about to discover.

A total of twelve weeks were set aside for the Frye hearings in the Castro case. That would be three months in which the scientific ins and outs of this complex new testing system would be pulled to bits and put back together again to ensure there were no glitches. It was too much for your average attorney to deal with. In fact, it was too much for anyone not totally versed in biochemistry to deal with. That's why, of course, no defence lawyer had even considered challenging it. New Jersey lawyer, Andrew Rossimer, a sole practitioner, was scheduled to defend Castro. But, before he could get anywhere near the question of who committed the murder, he would have to spend months knee-high in chemicals and genes. 'It's beyond what one attorney should have to do,' Rossimer said. 'I have to make a living.' He called in virtually the only two lawyers familiar with the technique in the state. Their names were Peter Neufeld and Barry Scheck and they were about to become very famous. Neufeld and Scheck were friends who had spent some of their early careers as defence lawyers in the Bronx Legal Aid Society. Neufeld went on to be a sole practitioner and Scheck became a legal academic but the two men remained close. At the time when the Castro hearings were looming large, Neufeld and Scheck had just been appointed to a new panel that had recently been set up to look at DNA testing in the state. The duo knew a little about DNA-testing techniques and they were keen to learn a lot more.

They started with the basics. They got Lifecodes to send them copies of the DNA prints, the x-ray photographs, or autorads, that had been made in the Castro case. These were the prints that showed a match between Vilma Ponce's sample and the blood found on Castro's watch. This was the match that the Lifecodes Corporation had described as having a 198,000,000-to-one chance of being wrong. The first thing they needed to do was to understand how Lifecodes, who were one of only three organisations in the United States doing DNA testing at the time, got their probabilities. At the time, DNA testing was a closed-off science. It just wasn't something that people could go along and see being done. Prosecutors sent samples to either Lifecodes or Cellmark Diagnostics (the FBI were just starting their own testing) who then sent the results back. Nobody, but nobody, questioned how it was done. It was too complex.

In truth, Lifecodes' system was pretty standard. Their radioactive probes landed on four different places on the enormous gene map. They weren't the same places as Alec Jeffreys' probes had alighted on but science was on a constant hunt now for good landing sites and that was really all that distinguished much of the testing. Indeed, an industry had sprung up selling just the probe part of the DNA testing kit.

Commercial organisations vied with each other to come up with probes that would fix on the sites delivering the cleanest results. Anyway, these places were known as loci and, in those loci, the probes were looking for things called alleles. Allele is just a fancy name for a bit of junk DNA. So, four sites were usually hit and the probes brought back several alleles to be chopped up and measured. The machines spewed out a piece of x-ray film called an autorad which contained the results of the test. It showed each of the alleles as a dark band running across the paper.

Now, the whole idea of DNA profiling is to compare one sample with another sample and to look for a match or a no match. To make that easier, the bands for both samples came out on the same bit of paper but separated into parallel channels. All that the scientists had to do was to look at the two side-by-side patterns for each allele and see if they matched. If all the allele bands in the two samples – and that could be up to eight bands – line up, then they are said to come from the same person. Of course, it is entirely possible that lots of different people will share one or two of the alleles or bands. For close relatives, this figure could be even higher. By checking all the samples in their database, the scientists work out how likely each band is to appear in the population and then they multiply the odds for each band together to give a total result. Just like an accumulator at horse racing. Simple. Sort of.

Neufeld and Scheck had their Castro autorads, showing the DNA profiles, but they weren't quite sure what they meant. So they took them to a seminar on DNA testing that people from the Lifecodes Corporation were attending. A lot of scientists were there and one in particular, a Dr Eric Lander, seemed to know what he was talking about. He quizzed the Lifecodes boys about some strange technical things that were going on with the samples they had brought along. Neufeld cornered Dr Lander in a kitchen where he was sitting with a number of other scientists and asked him to look at the Castro DNA autorads. The story goes that Lander then held an autorad up to a window and called his colleagues over for a look. 'Match or no match?' he asked them. Two of the three replied 'Garbage!' but the other said 'Do the test again.'. And this was what the prosecution claimed was the 198,000,000-to-one racing certainty.

After that little incident, the lawyers knew they were on to something. They pestered Dr Lander, a mathematician and human geneticist, to give them a hand. He wouldn't testify in court, he told them, but he'd point them in the right direction and look over their stuff. By now, the defence duo was hauling everything they could out of Lifecodes – documents, lab notes, you name it. They were looking for something. It was a phenomenon that they'd heard mentioned at the DNA seminar. It was something that had led the scientists in the room to shake their heads in dismay when they heard how Lifecodes treated it. It was called band-shifting. Nobody knew why it happened but the long and the short of it was that sometimes bands didn't match up exactly. Sometimes they shifted down their channel. But they were still called a match. A Lifecodes director had given the game away at that seminar on DNA technology when he suggested it wasn't a major problem. The question that was bugging Lander and the lawyers was how could you know whether there was a match or not match. When was it band-shifting – meaning it was a match – and when was it someone's else's DNA – meaning not a match at all? And how on earth did you decide when it was?

They had good reason to be extremely interested in it. They'd looked closely at the Castro DNA results and spotted right away there was not an exact match between the bands from Vilma Ponce's results and the bands from the blood found on the watchstrap. 'Band-shifting,' Lifecodes said. 'Nope,' the defence team replied. Lifecodes had explained in their literature that they had a formula which they could use to work out whether two bands were close enough to be called a match. Using that formula, they claimed that six bands from Vilma exactly matched six bands from the watchstrap. Yet, when the lawyers measured them, two of them weren't even within Lifecodes' own parameters. They were not matches at all. It got stranger. While being cross examined on the witness stand, Dr Michael Baird, the Lifecodes director, who had given the 'leaving your name, address and social security number' warning to criminals, admitted that the matching of the bands was done not by some scientific technique but by the human eye. Yet Lifecodes' own literature said that was not possible. Astonishingly, the DNA case against Castro was starting to come apart at the seams.

Then Barry Scheck discovered something on a routine visit to Lifecodes' offices. So far, the defence team had been working on copies of the DNA x-rays. Scheck got the original x-rays and laid them out on a table to have a look at them. He noticed something bizarre. Vilma Ponce's sample had three bands but the watchstrap stain had five. There were two extra bands that were not visible on the copies that had been given to the defence team. It looked like another devastating find. But, in court, Lifecodes managed to explain away the two extra bands as simply bacterial contamination.

That should have been the end of it. Grave doubts had been cast over the band-shifting phenomenon. Lifecodes had got themselves totally mixed up over whether they used the human eye to call a match or whether there actually was some scientific technique. And, of course, there were those bands that nothing – not the human eye nor any calculation – could have called a match. It would have been a pretty good result – good enough, maybe, to have the DNA evidence thrown out or at the least placed in serious doubt.

But the defence team wasn't going to let the matter rest there. In true Perry Mason style, they had a surprise up their sleeves. The surprise came in the form of one Professor Howard Cooke who was to burst on to the scene like the last-minute expert witness that television producers love to have in scripts. This was real life though and Professor Cooke was the scientist who had developed the probe used by Lifecodes. The probe that was responsible for the results on that autorad which showed the extra two bands. Appropriately enough, it was called Cooke's Probe. Professor Howard Cooke was a geneticist at the Medical Research Council Human Genetics Unit in Edinburgh, Scotland, more than 3,000 miles away. One overcast New York day, he walked into the Castro case hearings and blew the DNA evidence out of the water.

Many years after the event, Professor Cooke says his memory is shaky on the exact chain of events that saw him plucked from the lofty towers of Scottish academia and into the setting of a Bronx court. He remembers some of the details. 'I had worked on that particular DNA probe – 29C1 I think it was called. And I became involved in the case through a network, you might say. I happened to know a guy called Eric Lander who was connected to the Liberal New York Mafia. He wanted to know what I thought of the evidence. I was in Boston at the time, I think, at a conference. I travelled up to New York and had a look at it.'

Professor Cooke was persuaded to come along to the hearing and give evidence on the 'bacterial contamination' that made up the two extra lines in the blood taken from the watchstrap. He remembers that the court setting was very *Bonfire of the Vanities* but that the occasion wasn't overwhelming. He sat at a table, rather than from a witness stand, to give his evidence and the atmosphere was very relaxed. Well, it was relaxed before Professor Cooke spoke. Professor Cooke's testimony was straightforward and to the point. He didn't think that the two extra bands came from 'bacterial contamination' he told the court. They looked human. In fact, looking at the sample from Vilma Ponce and the sample from the blood on the watchstrap – samples that were supposed to be 198,000,000 times more likely to be a match than not – Professor Cooke said they weren't a match at all. It was an incredible result. Not only had the defence team managed to get the world's leading expert on that particular probe to come along and testify on their behalf but he had driven a stake right through the heart of the DNA evidence. And it only happened because, luckily, he had been in America at a conference just when the defence team needed a white knight to come charging to the rescue. On such coincidences history is made.

After the Professor's testimony, a special meeting of the scientific experts from both sides, along with Lifecodes' people too, met without lawyers to discuss what had happened. They issued a joint statement saying the DNA results 'were not reliable enough to support the assertion that the samples do or do not match'. DNA testing had been defeated. The judge ruled that, although he thought the system met the Frye Standard, the actual standards used by Lifecodes in their labs meant, in this particular case, it was inadmissible.

Along the way, a whole lot of other interesting facts about the infallible DNA tests had been dredged up. It emerged that, even if those blood samples had been a match, the amazing statistics of 198,000,000-to-one would have been wrong anyway. The defence had brought in evidence to show that, when four probes were used, Lifecodes' probability figures were wrongly stated by a factor of 160,000.

Dr Lander also gave evidence showing how easy it was to turn the statistical tables around. He showed that the chances of the alleles, which Lifecodes had matched visually, actually being the same were one in 1,500,000.

The knock-on effect of the Castro case was devastating. DNA profiling, the new dawn for forensic science, had suddenly and astonishingly been found wanting. Band-shifting, something hardly anyone had ever heard of, became a commonly discussed phenomenon. The ease with which Lifecodes, a company with supposedly rigorous laboratory standards, could make mistakes was frightening. In the light of this, the trust with which DNA results had been accepted in other cases appeared naive. There were now major question marks over convictions throughout the US.

As Peter Neufeld said, 'In the first two dozen cases where DNA evidence was introduced, the opposing attorney did not even challenge the evidence. They felt scientifically illiterate and unable to even perceive of questions. No adverse experts were even retained by the counsel. Everyone just sort of lay down and died.'

If Castro were to happen today, there would be uproar, appeals and possibly some sort of public inquiry. In the US of the late '80s, only the public inquiry was to transpire. The reason other cases weren't pulled apart and dissected was quite simple – apart from Neufeld and Scheck, the legal profession was still almost totally ignorant of DNA profiling. Many, many cases had not even gone to court. A year after the Castro verdict, Peter Neufeld said that DNA evidence had featured in up to 1,000 cases in the US. In the majority of cases, the accused and his or her defence team had no way of challenging the results and pled guilty rather than go to trial.

What of Timothy W Spencer? He had gone to the electric chair protesting his innocence. Nobody believed a word of it and, since then, nothing has been turned up to indicate he wasn't guilty. His lawyers had asked for the DNA evidence against him to be retested as the clock ticked down to his execution. The request was refused. It really wasn't thought necessary.

People started to speak out against DNA testing. Strange occurrences began to be reported in the press. Stories began to appear that indicated that it wasn't just that people couldn't be bothered to challenge DNA testing – they weren't allowed to.

The New York Times ran a piece saying that top molecular biologists believed DNA testing was not sufficiently reliable to be used in court. Critics included Dr Thomas G Marr, a molecular biologist at Cold Spring Harbor Laboratory on Long Island. He said, 'Before I'd start convicting people based on this technology, I'd want to study it in much greater detail. There are several reasons, both theoretical and practical, that justify careful attention being paid to this.'

Dr James W Geyer, a founder of Genetic Design Inc. in Greensboro, NC, said, 'The literature on this technology is still very thin. There's an awful lot of marketing going on.' He claimed that DNA testing in paternity cases was wrong two per cent of the time. He knew it was wrong, he said, because he had sent the same samples to two DNA labs and he went on to outline an alarming example. One laboratory would say the person the sample came from was definitely the father – putting astronomically high odds against this being the case. The other laboratory would say that the person the sample came from was definitely not the father – again, substantiating their claim with astronomically high odds.

In one case, Dr Geyer revealed a laboratory had said that not only was the father not the father but the mother was not the mother. When he told the laboratory that maternity was not an issue, the laboratory came back and said the mother was the mother and the father was the father.

Dr Geyer's laboratory had recently started doing its own forensic DNA profiling, using the system developed by the FBI. Of the first 1,000 samples, he was sure five per cent were wrong. All the DNA profiling systems, whether used by the FBI, the Home Office in Britain or the commercial companies, were essentially the same. Minor details, such as the make up of probes and the sites examined, were all that varied.

It wasn't easy criticising the new system. Scientists start to pop up all over the place saying that, when they had tried to question the accuracy of DNA profiling, the authorities had gagged them. One was Dr Simon Ford, who said that, under cross-examination during a case, an FBI lawyer had started to question the status of his US work visa. The experience, he added, had put him off testifying in other trials.

Another scientist, Dr Laurence Mueller of the University of California at Irvine, said a Federal prosecutor had threatened him. Others said agents of the Federal Bureau of Investigation had called them and told them how damaging it would be for the prosecution if they testify for the defence in criminal trials involving DNA evidence.

One of the most powerful claims came from a Dr Daniel Hartl of Washington University in St. Louis. He said a Federal prosecutor, from the Justice Department's Strike Force in Cleveland, had pressured him to withdraw an article that was due to appear in the journal *Science*. Dr Hartl and his co-author, Dr Richard Lewontin of Harvard University, claimed they were forced by the journal's editor, at the last minute, to soften their conclusions that the statistical basis for calculating the accuracy of DNA fingerprints was fatally flawed. Of course, the unreliability of DNA statistics had already been exposed during the Castro trial. Nevertheless, the publication of the article was delayed while the journal solicited a rebuttal. The rebuttal, which was published along with the article, denied every point made by the critics.

Legal experts were reported to be concerned about a pattern of intimidation aimed at scientists. 'This has me very upset,' Dr William Thompson, an associate professor of criminology, law and society at the University of California at Irvine, was quoted in *The New York Times* as saying. 'I've never seen anything like this before.'

Such allegations, coming hard on the heels of the Castro case, could have dealt a fatal blow to the new system. They could, perhaps, have stopped the whole forensic scene in its tracks. But they didn't. DNA profiling couldn't be killed off. It was too late. There was far too much at stake for the private corporations, who had invested heavily in its success and were just about to do battle over the spoils. There was too much at stake for the law enforcement community who knew full well that, with a couple of tweaks, they had a knockout weapon at their fingerprints. There was also too much at stake for the scientific community who were already relying heavily on DNA profiling and polymerase chain reaction (PCR) in the fight to diagnose and contain some of humankind's most frightening diseases. The Castro case turned out to be a setback – nothing more.

However, there was an interesting footnote to it. Castro's trial went ahead without the DNA evidence from the watchstrap. As a result, the prosecutors were so concerned that they would not get a conviction that they offered a plea bargain to Castro. He would receive a sentence of twenty years to life. He accepted the deal. He also confirmed that the blood on the watchstrap had, in fact, come from Vilma Ponce.

6

THE GRAVE

Red, black and white, the colours of death, the flags, the shouting, the screaming, the children, the rivers of blood, the horror – the absolute horror. All of it conjured up by his bones, the bones lying in Alec Jeffreys' office at Leicester University, the bones sitting on the very desk facing the wall where the scientist worked every day. Dr Jeffreys had seen some strange things in his time – things that he would never have expected to have had to deal with when he embarked on his academic career – things that most policemen would not normally come upon in a lifetime of dealing with depravity, things that most people wouldn't even stumble on in their nightmares. Yet, this was the strangest. 'Spooky,' Jeffreys says, as he casts his mind back to the day they arrived and goes over the experience of having them lying there before him, of touching them, of handling them, of knowing what they might mean. 'Just spooky.'

It had taken years for the bones to arrive in his office. Years when they were lying around and being poked and prodded. Years when half the world, it seemed, was arguing over them. But who could have foreseen that, when the story began on the spring morning of 31 May 1985, just as the sun rose over the little town of Günzburg, in Bavaria, Germany, when Hans Sedlmeier, the outwardly respectable sales manager of a local factory that manufactured farm machinery, opened his door to a squad of policemen and a search warrant. He may have professed outrage or innocence, anger or surprise. If he did, he was a liar. The game had begun. What was discovered among the papers in Sedlmeier's house was enough to spark a hunt that would cover thousands of miles and end up beneath the hard-baked soil of a graveyard on the other side of the Atlantic Ocean. It was only a name and an address but it was the beginning of the end of the mystery.

That name was Simon Weidelmain and that address was in the city of Sao Paolo, Brazil. So Weidelmain got the knock too. The police took more papers, more names. Addresses. They were getting closer. They moved on, following the clumsy paper trail across the city to the homes of two couples of European extraction. Their names were Wolfram and Liselotte Bossart and Gitta and Geza Stammer. Maybe it was the burden of carrying the secret or maybe it was because they knew that the game wasn't worth the candle. Whatever. When the police turned up at their doors, they started talking about him and they talked plenty. They were scared and so they should have been.

The Stammers took the police to a grim, little yellow bungalow they owned at 5555 Alvarenga Road, in the suburb of Eldorado on the outskirts of Sao Paolo. It was where he had lived. Of course, he wasn't there. But they poked around the place, looked down the well in the back garden, walked around the three tiny rooms, heard about the twenty-four inch black and white Telefunken television that he had bought in a desperate attempt to relieve the suffocating emptiness in his life. They found diaries – some more blanks in his life were filled in. They moved on.

The resort of Bertioga lies twenty-five miles south of Sao Paolo. It was where the Bossarts owned a tiny two-bedroom house, right on the shore. It was the next stop for the police. They all went down to the beach and stood by the rocks and the Bossarts gesticulated at the water, just a few feet out, then pointed to a patch of sand. Right beside them. That's where it happened. They said it was around four o'clock in the afternoon of 7 February 1979. He had been sitting on the rocks, talking, moping really, going on about Günzburg and going home. Then he'd gone for a swim. Andreas Bossart, their son, had seen him thrashing about in the water and shouted, 'Uncle, watch the current!' By the time Gitta Bossart had waded in and reached him the thrashing had stopped. He was lying on the surface like a sick fish – sideways. They dragged him out but he was dying. And then he was dead. Just like that – no trial, no retribution, no justice, no noose.

But it wasn't quite the end of the search. They wanted to see his body, naturally. It wasn't far away, or so the Bossarts and Stammers said, not far at all. So they all got back in the cars and out on to the highway and drove along to Embu Cemetery. Then they walked along the rows of headstones until they found plot number 321. The headstone said it contained one Wolfgang Gerhard, a German national who had drowned on 7 February 1979 at Bertioga. But it couldn't have been Gerhard's body because he was already dead by that time. He had died in 1978 in Austria. So who was in the grave? Who had really drowned that afternoon on the beach after suffering a stroke whilst swimming? Whose crimes were so great that, almost forty years after he had committed them, millions of people would sit glued to their televisions as hard, dry soil was opened up and his bones, the ones which ended up on Alec Jeffreys' desk, were spilled out into the baking sun. It wasn't Wolfgang Gerhard. That was an alias. It wasn't Fritz Ullman, Fritz Hollman, Helmut Gregor, G Helmuth, Ludwig Gregor or even Jose Mengele. Every one of those names was an alias he used during his thirty-three years on the run, aliases used to cover the fact that he was more commonly known as the Angel of Death or the Great Selector. His real name was, of course, Josef Mengele, the butcher of Auschwitz. His days of running were finally over.

In 1985, when the police had turned up at Hans Sedlmeier's house, the Mengele family firm, where he worked, was still going strong. Sedlmeier was company secretary at Karl Mengele & Sohne, a $100m dollar-a-year business which was also the biggest employer in Günzburg. Banner adverts on the main roads leading into the town proudly proclaimed Mengele's was the place to go if you wanted the best in agricultural machinery. What it didn't proclaim was that it was also where much of the funds to keep Josef Mengele on the run came from – channelled to the war criminal by the outwardly respectable Sedlemeier.

Before the war, Josef's father, Karl, had wanted young Josef to join the family firm. He had wanted him to become an accountant – to be precise, go to university, then come back home and help do the books at Mengele's. But Josef was set on becoming a doctor and Josef usually got his own way. So that's what he did. He went to university, he got a couple of degrees and he completed a PhD. His thesis was a study on the way jaw shapes could be used to determine race. Then the war started and Mengele joined the Waffen-SS and served at the front where he was decorated twice. In fact, he got an Iron Cross first class for pulling two German soldiers out of a blazing tank. He was a regular hero. They were all proud. He was good looking too. So

95

handsome, they said later at Auschwitz, so immaculately dressed, so distinguished, as he wandered around the trains selecting who would live and who would die, pulling the children, especially twins, he loved twins, away from their parents. 'Zwillings!' he'd shout. 'Twins!' These weren't your run-of-the-mill medical experiments. He didn't use anaesthetics for a start. He didn't do anything you'd find in the medical textbooks, anything he'd learned about at the Universities of Frankfurt or Munich (though at least one of his professors had taught him that only perfect human beings were worth saving and it was his duty to get rid of the rest). He injected dye into the children's eyes to try to make them blue, injected other things into their organs, their hearts, all without anaesthetic. He sewed children together and left them to die horrible gangrenous deaths. He deliberately infected others. He marked the Jewish festival of Yom Kippur by gassing 1000 boys and girls together. The list of things he did in the name of medicine was breathtaking in its awfulness and cruelty. Still their parents weren't going to complain. They were already dead.

He looked like that American movie star Clark Gable, they remembered. So handsome. And they did remember. Lots of them remembered. And they told, they shouted, they screamed. So that, when the war was over, just over, his name was already on the list of war criminals wanted by the Americans. His name was on the list, all right, the list of those who would swing for what they had done.

But the aftermath of war is chaos. And, in the chaos, Mengele, although held in an American camp under his own name, walked free. He worked on a farm in Germany owned by a family called the Fischers for years, right under the noses of the occupying forces. Then he skipped to South America. He lived in Argentina, under a string of aliases, but the Angel of Death slowly realised that the authorities had forgotten him and he relaxed. He became bold. So bold that, in 1954, he divorced his wife in Germany, legally, using his own name – his real name. So bold, that his father ventured a trip to Argentina to visit him. So bold, that he legally ditched his Argentinian alias and had the Argentinian authorities officially recognize his real name. Incredible to think of now but utterly true. And he got away with it. Nothing happened. He even travelled back to Europe to meet the son who had been only one year old when he fled, the same son who, so many years later, would play a crucial role in identifying him. During that meeting in Switzerland, Josef Mengele courted his dead brother's wife, Martha. His father, Karl, had suggested the liaison, to keep the family firm's shares in family hands. She came to Argentina and married him. It seemed as though the stench of the concentration camp no longer hung over Josef Mengele. For the Family Mengele, life went on as though the war had never happened.

But it was all too much. One of the victims of his cruelty started asking questions, found the divorce papers, alerted the authorities. The balloon was finally up. In 1959, the West Germans issued a warrant for his arrest. His universities, the universities of Frankfurt and Munich, withdrew his degrees. Still, people had looked for him before and nothing had happened. He wasn't unduly worried. Then, in 1960, Mengele's world crumbled. The Israelis kidnapped Adolf Eichmann, took him from South America to Israel and hanged him by the neck until he was dead. Mengele was next. He knew it and he was terrified. It was time to run again. He moved and moved again, staying with Nazi sympathisers in a German colony, staying with Nazi sympathisers in Paraguay, where he was granted citizenship. But pressure was mounting. Nowhere was safe. He fled to Brazil, took a partnership in a farm, started using aliases again. It worked for a while but that's all. Things started falling apart. The money was drying up. His second wife returned to Germany. Eventually, he ended up in Sao Paolo, struggling to get by financially, with friends he paid to keep their mouths shut, living in that little yellow rented house.

And so he survived in fear and terror, lonely and desperate until, on 5 February 1979, he boarded a bus alone and headed down to the beach to spend a couple of days with the Bossarts. It took him two hot, hellish hours to get there and he was already sick. He'd had a minor stroke before. When he arrived, he was aggressive and angry and talking of going home. Home to Germany of all places. He stayed in the house for two days, only coming out on the seventh to wander a little on the beach, to ramble on about going back to Günzburg and writing a history of the town – and then he went for that swim. His last ever swim.

The exhumation was a bit of a circus. The world watched and waited to see if the bones in Embu graveyard really did belong to

Mengele. But it wasn't that easy to tell. The Brazilians, embarrassed by the fact that they had had the most notorious living Nazi under their noses, were not keen to let anyone else take over. They insisted on carrying out the identification themselves. They took his bones and measured them, they worked out the age of them, they compared them to the known facts on Josef Mengele. They took a photograph of his skull and projected it on to a television screen Then they took a video of Mengele, made when he was alive, and placed that over it. They matched the eyes and they matched the mouth. They matched twenty-eight points on the skull and they pretty well reckoned they had matched Mengele to the bones. The US consul general in Brazil put the tin lid on it though. Stephen Dachi had been a dental pathologist before becoming involved in the diplomatic service. He was sitting reading through the diaries taken from Mengele's house when he noticed a dental appointment mentioned along with a code word for the dentist. There were no dental records in Mengele's Nazi file. The Nazi's had destroyed everything as the Allies approached. But Dachi knew that, if he could find the dentist, which he did, then he could compare the x-rays with the teeth on the body. He shouldn't have been involved at all but he managed to persuade the Brazilians to let him try. The x-rays matched the body. It was over. The world was told Mengele was dead. And that should have been the end of the story.

But nothing is that simple where evil war criminals are involved. The Israelis, though they said nothing, were not convinced. It was too pat, too perfect, too convenient, they thought. They were well aware that the year the body had been found was also, coincidentally, the year Mengele had been publicly tried, in absentia, in Israel. That a £2 million reward had been placed on his head. That the pressure had been stepped up. There was worldwide publicity of his crimes, which gave impetus to the hunt. What a coincidence that he had died in that same year, they thought. And hadn't it been suspiciously easy to follow the trail from Mengele's home town all the way to that Brazilian graveyard? All his associates had talked when pressurised – most of them had incriminating documents leading straight to the body. And then there were those perfect diaries. True, they were authenticated as being in Mengele's handwriting. But what if he was still alive and had faked them himself? Had it all been an elaborate plot by the Angel of

Death to cover his tracks once more?

Israeli police colonel, Menachem Russek, thought so. He had gone to Brazil and investigated the claims. His secret report demolished them. Why had Liselotte Bossart claimed Mengele had had a stroke in the sea, then later, apparently, denied denied that story? Why had she alone taken the body to the cemetery on the night of 11 February? Why had none of Mengele's circle ever seen it? Why was there no record of a coffin being sold that night? The colonel also looked at Stephen Dachi's dental evidence. Fine, he said, except for one thing. There was absolutely no proof that the x-rays in the dentist's office had come from Mengele. As such, the claimed match was nonsense. Israeli doctors examined the case. In 1989, one of them, Dr Maurice Rogev, said the identification of the body was 'bloody nonsense'. His official report to the Israeli government mentioned that Nazi records described Mengele's skull as measuring 57 centimetres but the one in the coffin measured 50.5 centimetres. There was also no sign on the bones of osteomyelitis, a disease Mengele was known to have suffered from when young. A disease that should have left telltale scarring. Strangest of all, the Mengele family in Germany, who had funded Josef's flight from justice, who had kept in contact all the time, had never asked for the Angel of Death's remains. It was all looking like a massive set-up. Even the great Israeli Nazi hunter, Dr Simon Wiesenthal, who had originally been convinced, changed his mind after hearing of the official suspicions. The doubts leaked out in the late '80s. The cat was out of the bag. The mystery of Josef Mengele's disappearance had not been solved at all. He'd merely slipped the noose once more.

But not everyone subscribed to the conspiracy theory. The West Germans had led the hunt for Mengele and they weren't about to give up overnight. They decided to order tests using the latest scientific techniques. And that's when Dr Alec Jeffreys and Dr Erika Hagelberg stepped in. They had already been down this road before with the body of Karen Price – in fact, both cases overlapped slightly. But it was going to be even harder this time. That hot Brazilian climate had had an extremely degrading effect on the 'Mengele' remains. The slivers of bone that Erika Hagelberg removed and Dr Jeffreys had on his desk before him were of extremely poor quality. The DNA had broken down – there was absolutely no way that single-locus profiling would produce enough material to give a meaningful result. They could try to use Kary Mullis's technique, nature's photocopier, PCR. The trouble was that PCR gave ridiculously poor results – five-to-one, twelve-to-one certainties, that sort of thing. That wasn't going to convince anyone. But there was a solution at hand. It was a new DNA profiling method that would come to the rescue, just when the science was at its lowest ebb. And everybody knew the science was at an extremely low ebb. Of that there could be little doubt. While the Mengele hunt had been going on, the ripples emanating from the Castro case had also been making themselves felt. They had now become roaring breakers, upsetting all the accepted facts, shattering the legal confidence in the new system. The field of criminal DNA profiling had been left in almost total disarray. There were hearings into its effectiveness in America and a significant number of states banned the technique from court altogether. There were grave doubts about whether commercial laboratories could be trusted to carry out the tests properly and, of course, there were serious misgivings about the way statistics were being used to calculate matches.

The controversy over an article in *Science* by Richard Lewontin and Daniel Hartl, the two scientists who protested that they were being gagged by the authorities, had reached a peak. They had pointed out that there was no justification for claiming odds of one in millions when the databases of DNA profiles that these astronomical figures were based on were tiny. How, the men asked, could anyone say there was a one in a billion chance of a profile being matched when the number of people actually profiled in the US was only in the hundreds? They insisted that the method used to work out how likely particular profiles were to crop up in society was deeply flawed because it didn't take account of different ethnic groups. It was damning stuff. In response, the FBI changed the way its fledgling DNA unit calculated odds.

But the world hadn't stood still since Alec Jeffreys had come up with DNA fingerprinting. It had even moved on in the short time since Neufeld and Scheck had punched giant holes in the Castro case.

In the small town of Marshfield in Wisconsin, an American geneticist had come up with something that would eventually change the face of DNA profiling and pull the fledgling science's singed reputation from the fire. Dr James Weber and his wife had moved to Marshfield for a number of reasons. Quality of life for their children was one of them. The mild climate was another. Neither of them liked living in hot places and they'd actually drawn a line across a map of the states, delineating the hottest areas and vowing, wherever they'd go, it was going to be somewhere mild. Marshfield was also close to where Dr Weber had grown up and gone to school and he wanted to live in the kind of place where you knew your neighbours. His colleagues thought he was nuts. Nobody in their right mind abandoned the major research centres for an unknown private research school like Marshfield College of Medicine. But Jim Weber wasn't nuts. If Marshfield wasn't on the map when he arrived, he would put it on it. Within two short years he had done just that.

The way he achieved it was to discover, in 1988, a new type of DNA marker called short tandem repeats. Short tandem repeats differed from long tandem repeats, the type of markers Alec Jeffreys originally used, because they were, quite simply, shorter, tougher and more abundant. That meant they could be found on samples which were extremely degraded and were even recoverable from samples where the DNA was broken down. They had another fantastic advantage. They worked exceptionally well with the PCR genetic photocopying system. And then there was the killer application. The one that would eventually, years in the future, blow all the others out of the water and solve one of the biggest problems facing DNA typing – it looked like it would be possible to automate the testing process.

At the time when Alec Jeffreys was examining bone that possibly belonged to one of World War II's greatest criminals, the new technique was being tried out on the victims of another war, the Persian Gulf War. The US had never really got over the failure to adequately identify those killed in the Vietnam War and, more than twenty years after that conflict ended, the fate of those missing in action (MIAs) still haunted the nation. The Gulf War was going to be different. Nobody would be unidentified, nobody would be forgotten. Casualties were nowhere near as high as in Vietnam but they were significant and often proved hard to identify. The United States Army lost thirty-three men in action during the Gulf War. Hardest hit was the 16th Special Operations Squadron and not all deaths came from enemy fire. In total, across all the services, ninety-six men were killed in action and a further fifty were killed by friendly fire. Identification of casualties had to be quick and accurate. DNA profiling seemed a God-given tool. But the application of single-locus probes was limited because of the large pieces of DNA needed. PCR was also weak because it gave very low levels of accuracy. It was decided to test using the new short tandem repeats (STRs) that Jim Weber had come up with. The exercise was hugely successful. So successful that it was just a matter of time before they would be used in criminal investigations.

Jim Weber is one of the unsung heroes of the DNA-fingerprinting revolution. His achievements are recognized by his peers but, in the wider world, the answer to the question of who discovered STRs is not one that trips off the tongue of many people. In fact, such has been the explosion in STR research that Jim Weber's achievement has been kind of lost in all the detail. This is because, once short tandem repeats, which are simply points of the DNA chain, had been identified, the race was on to find the ones that gave the best results for different applications. Alec Jeffreys actually used a limited set he had come up with himself in conjunction with some from Jim Weber's lab to help in the identification of Karen Price. It went largely unnoticed. By the time he had moved on to Mengele, a different set of markers was being tried. Everybody was looking for the ones that had the most discriminating power, the set that would enable the scientists to say, 'this person is almost unique'. Today, literally thousands of STRs have been identified and they are used in different combinations for different purposes right across the medical, scientific and forensic fields. Count-less combinations of STRs have been patented by companies and are used in different genetic testing kits.

When tracked down to his office at Marshfield, Dr Weber is typically sanguine about his achievement. 'Yes, I discovered STRs around the end of 1987,' he says. 'We presented our results at meetings in 1988 and published them in 1989.' The discovery first appeared in the *American Journal of Human Genetics* under the heading 'Abundant class of human DNA polymorphisms which can be typed using the polymerase chain reaction'. Patents followed shortly after its publication. Dr Weber credits Alec Jeffreys as the inspiration for much of his work. 'There were plenty of clues already available at the time of discovery, especially in Alec Jeffreys' work. I will take credit, however, for aggressive exploitation of the discovery, which I think was important.'

Dr Weber regards their impact on the world of criminal forensics with some bemusement because he has never done any work in the field. 'The discovery certainly had a great impact on forensics and genetics in general but I can't claim a tremendous amount of insight. Alec and others have taken the lead in that area,' he adds. 'My research has focused on their application in disease gene hunting, genomics, clinical genetics and, to a lesser degree, human evolution.'

So, it was the work of a number of scientists, such as Alec Jeffreys, Jim Weber, Erika Hagelberg and many others, that was used to try to finally identify one of history's most evil pseudo-scientists. It had become an extremely high profile task. As Dr Jeffreys used STRs to try to identify those bones in his office, the arguments raged about who had really been found in Embu. The fate of the Nazi had, by now, become the subject of the conspiracy theorists. Like Elvis, Lord Lucan and Jim Morrison, few really believed Mengele was dead.

The eyes of the world focused on the little lab at Leicester University waiting for a puff of smoke to signal one way or the other what was going on. But it wasn't that straightforward. There was one major problem. Dr Jeffreys had no problem getting a profile from the bones. But he did not have any sample from Mengele to compare those results with. The obvious answer was to go to Mengele's son, now known as Rolf Jenkel, a property developer living in Germany. Rolf had changed his name and had not been close to his father after that fleeting meeting in Switzerland when he was a child. For that reason, it wasn't thought likely there would be a problem. He had gone to visit Mengele eight weeks before he died. The purpose of the trip had been to see if there was any spark of familial love there. The answer, Rolf claimed, was no. Yet, for some peculiar reason, Rolf was not willing to submit the blood sample that was needed to end one of the world's greatest mysteries. It looked as though Mengele was going to have the last laugh. Meanwhile, the Israelis revealed they were actively investigating a Josef Mengele sighting on another continent. Embarrassment loomed.

But, yet again, the German authorities were not willing to be sidestepped. They discreetly warned that, if Rolf didn't provide a DNA sample, then they'd dig up his grandparents, his great-grandparents and they'd keep on digging until they found a relative whose body was in a decent enough state to provide a sample. The pressure worked. Rolf Jenkel caved in and gave a sample. Alec Jeffreys ran it through the tests and compared it to the other results. In 1992, he reported to his clients, the West German government, that he had a result. It wasn't the one the world now expected. They called a press conference to say that the body found in the grave in Sao Paolo was, indeed, that of Josef Mengele. Of that Dr Jeffreys was 99 per cent certain. Even the Israelis accepted the veracity of the tests. At long last Josef Mengele was really dead.

The short tandem repeat system had been a stunning success in providing profiles, quickly and accurately, from very degraded human samples. But, so far, its forensic use had been confined to the lab of Dr Jeffreys, who was, after all, the world's leading authority on DNA profiling. The next step would be to get it out into the hands of the police and investigating authorities. It didn't take long.

It's summer in the city, Los Angeles, 1991. It's roasting hot and Jack Unterweger is in the back of an LAPD patrol car, seeing at first hand that not everybody lives the dream. The prostitutes are at their pitches, the streets are littered with rubbish – it ain't Rodeo Drive. As the officers cruise slowly through the wasteland, they point out the sights to the famous author in the rear, giving him colour, flavour for the article he'll write when he returns to Vienna. And what flavour. During Jack's three-week stay no less than three prostitutes are murdered in Los Angeles – dragged from the streets and left to rot. Shannon Exley, thirty-five, Irene Rodriguez, thirty-three, and Peggy Jean Booth, twenty-six, had their names added to an endless litany of casualties. Victims of the American Dream. It's an irony Jack doesn't miss and, when he returns home, he pens these words. 'Real life in LA is dominated by a tough struggle for survival, by the broken dreams of thousands who come to the city and an equal number who leave, sometimes dead.'

As he does the talk show circuit, Jack Unterweger weaves the experience of what he has seen into his comments. He holds up the seedy side of life to the comfortable, cosy middle classes in his home country. He reminds them it happens in their cities too. Jack has seen it all in his time. Author of two prize-winning books, subject of a prize-winning film, he's one of Austria's most famous personalities. He's a darling of the intellectual circle, acting as their means of entry into a world they can never visit. His speciality is slime – to walk with the forgotten people who eke out a living in the twilight zone. to this end, following Czechoslovakia's 'velvet revolution', he went to Prague where he talked to the local prostitutes and heard how they can be cut down, murdered, just like in Los Angeles, and he sympathised with them. He has done the same in Austria where the prostitute murder rate is even higher. Jack is an expert – a special type of expert because he has been there and not just as a visitor.

Almost twenty years before, when he was young and brutish, he crossed the line. He murdered an eighteen-year-old girl. He saw his evil mother's face in hers and so strangled her with her underwear – her bra, in fact. It was senseless, it was stupid and he was caught. But that's not just where his fame comes from. So many people commit murders nowadays, that could never just be it. Jack is famous because Jack reformed in prison, he educated himself, he expressed himself and he found what he was looking for – redemption. When he was finally released after a long campaign by his supporters, the governor of the prison said, 'We will never find a man so well prepared for freedom.' True, everybody agreed. And, thank God. At last, someone had broken the cycle of crime, punishment and then more crime.

Jack's old life is long gone and he has embraced his new life with both arms. He is witty, clever and utterly reformed. He is living proof that the degrading consequences of a life in the gutter need not be permanent. Jack has washed away the sins and proved that the beast inside every man can be tamed. So who better to help the police track down a serial killer who is on the loose in Austria than Jack? And what a serial killer it was. The facts are astonishing. Seven deaths – Brunhilde Masser, thirty-nine, Hiedi Hammerer, thirty-one, Elfriede Schrempf, thirty-five, Silvia Zagler, twenty-three, Sabine Moitzel, twenty-five, Karine Eroglu-Sladky, twenty-five and Regina Prem, thirty-two – all wiped out in a space of just six months. Austria is no less crime-ridden than any other European country. But this was exceptional. And the police are way out of their depth. Everyone knows that. They need Jack's input.

Unfortunately, Jack can't help the police right now. Because Jack's back in the old US of A with his young girlfriend. And that's a major drawback. Because the police really want to ask him if it is just a coincidence that another murder, that of Blanka Bockova in Prague, took place when Jack was also in Prague researching an article. That was just four months after he was released from prison. The police would also like to ask him if he thinks it's a coincidence that the others, all found outside Vienna or Graz during the next six months, were strangled with – wait for it – their underwear. Yep, just like that girl he killed all those years ago. And there's that other thing – those three prostitutes who died when Jack was in Los Angeles. They were strangled with their bras too. Weird. It's certainly an amazing coincidence that, whenever a prostitute dies, Jack ain't far away.

Anyway, Jack's in Florida. And he's staying there. Everyone knows that because he phoned a newspaper to say they were all barking up the wrong tree. *The Kurier* told the world by printing the headline 'Hello, it's me the mass murderer'. Funny sense of humour those Austrians. But Jack couldn't have done it. Peter Huemer, a talk show host and writer who befriended Jack says so. 'If he was the killer, then he would be one of the cases of the century,' Huemer insists. 'Statistically, the chance that I would know one of the cases of the century is so unlikely that, therefore, I think he is not guilty.' And Peter Heumer is not joking. Apparently.

Jack had an unconventional childhood. His mother was a prostitute, he said. His father was an American GI who deserted Jack's mother who, in turn, deserted the child. It was institution after institution for young Jack, interspersed with spells with his alcoholic grandfather and a prostitute aunt. As soon as he was old enough, he drifted and plunged head first into the underworld with its drugs and whores and crimes. He had murdered Margaret Schafer, back in 1976, because of his mother, he said. He saw his mother's face flash before him, he told the court. In prison, something had flowered within him, they said. He began to write. It was cathartic. It destroyed the anger. And, boy, did he write. He wrote like a man possessed, said one of his contemporaries. First a prison magazine, then came his most famous book, *Trip to Jail – Report of a Guilty Man*. Jack was made. Intellectuals, politicians, psychologists queued up to back the campaign to have him released early from prison. He was a star.

Not everyone was convinced though. A retired Austrian detective, called August Schenner, had been banging on about a prostitute called Monica Horvarth, even while Jack was still inside. Monica, twenty-three, had been murdered and dumped in a pool in Salzburg in 1973. He was convinced Jack had done it. But, hey, the world's full of batty old policemen. Nobody was interested. Anyway, Jack was hot. Austrian society women used to send letters to him begging him to do things to them, sexual things, pornographic things. He had enormous presence. In the glittering Graz café society, they said that, when Jack walked in a room, you could feel his presence even when your back was turned to him. Presence was what he had in Miami where he was hiding out. Too much of it. It was presence and a string of credit card receipts that led the American police straight to him. When they picked him up, they said he just looked like a tourist. Sure, there was a bit of to-ing a fro-ing about extradition. Then he was back. Handcuffed, led off the plane and straight into to prison.

In his absence, the Austrians, not generally known for their liberalism, had cleaned up their act. They wanted the trial to be fair. They'd amassed 20,000 pages of evidence. The government warned the media to stop acting like Jack was guilty – to wait until he had actually been tried before they went crazy. They'd had a word with the police as well. Pointed out to them that maybe calling the 'unknown' suspect Jack the Strangler, before the man had even been arrested, wasn't the smartest move in the world.

Truth was there was a deal of nervousness. There wasn't a single piece of evidence linking Jack to any of these murders – not a fingerprint. Nothing. Of course, it would have been an extraordinary coincidence if it wasn't true. A set-up of mind-boggling complexity. But trials need proof. And the police weren't going to blow this one. They weren't exactly held in high public esteem anyway. Certainly not after it emerged that old August Schenner had gone straight to them when the first two prostitutes had been murdered and said it had to be Jack. Oops. A few more women had died before they got their act together.

And there was another thing. You could almost trace it to the point where Jack got off that plane and headed back to prison. There was a change in the public mood. People had actually started to doubt whether Jack had done it at all. After all, it all fitted into place extraordinarily neatly. Didn't it? Even the dumbest cop in the world would surely, eventually, have found his way to Jack's door with all those clues hanging about. And, if Jack had done it, surely he would have come up with a few alibis. One even. Because you only need an alibi for one murder to clear yourself of all the others when it is a serial killer case. Jack had no alibis. Not one. Well, not one he knew of.

But, curiously, it turned out he did have an alibi. He just didn't realise it. A few fans came forward to confirm that, on the night of 7 March 1991, at almost exactly the time Elfriede Schrempf was murdered, Jack had been thirty-minute drive away from the crime scene, giving a poetry reading. He wouldn't have – couldn't have – had time to drive there. That alibi hung in the air like a giant question mark over the whole affair for days. Then, suddenly, just like that, the police changed the time of Elfriede's disappearance.

No alibi again. But there was also still no solid evidence linking Jack to the girls. That's why the police were touring scrap yards looking for Jack's old car. They found it. It was the BMW he had been in when he had driven in Prague at the time of the murder there. Well, they found most of it. But, strangely, the seats were missing. They hunted for them too. And, you know what, and this is truly amazing, they found them, too, in the lock-up garage where they had been sitting for eighteen months. Then they discovered some things in the front passenger seat. They pulled off the seat cover and there, nestling under it, were a few human hairs. Who did they belong to? Jack? One of the girls? Were they evidence? There was only one way to find out. Use DNA typing.

Jack would publicly proclaim that he just did not understand this DNA stuff. Which wasn't an unreasonable point to make. It was, unfortunately, just a little bit irrelevant. Who cared whether Jack understood it? But it was, perhaps, just as well Jack didn't realise exactly what was going on because he was about to become one of the first people in the world to be examined using DNA's deadly new cocktail of three separate tests. Three tests that, between them, would nail down exactly what had been going on.

Naturally, the first thing the police did, in July 1992, was to send the hairs to the Scientific Police Institute in Zurich, Switzerland. They discovered that, under the microscope, three of the hairs looked exactly the same as Blanka Bockova's hairs. Interesting but hardly enough to convict a man. But, fortunately, all three hairs still had their roots, or sheaths, attached to them. They were delicately sliced into one-centimetre portions and, using phenol, subjected to a process to extract the DNA. It worked with just one of the hairs yielding a tiny two nanograms of material. This precious material was subjected to one of the most basic DNA tests, using a multi-locus probe.

The results were hardly earth shattering. There was a one-in-thirteen chance it had come from the head of Blanka Bockova. The sample of DNA material used in the first test was then purified and subjected to the PCR, genetic photocopying system, to produce enough material for a new test. This time the PCR system focused on five different DNA loci and returned a match with a result of one-in-2300. It was better but still not great. The Swiss police did not, yet, have a strong enough match to prove anything conclusively. But help was just around the corner.

In June 1994, they got their hands on a new system called GenePrint which was based on the emerging short tandem repeat method. This was the new dawn of automation. Basically, the system focused on three STR loci, or points, which had been selected by scientists because of their unusual characteristics. Only one nanogram of DNA material was needed to produce a match. It revealed that the odds on the hair not belonging to Blanka Bockova were one-in-2.3-million. The Swiss authorities now had a case. To double-check that there were no mistakes, they bypassed Blanka Bockova's samples and took DNA material from her parents. Yet again, there was a match.

Jack didn't understand the DNA evidence. He said so at his trial. But the jury did. They found him guilty of the murders of nine women and sentenced him to life imprisonment. But Jack, like Josef Mengele, had the last laugh. At 9 p.m., he was read the verdict of the court and sentenced to life imprisonment. His immediate reaction was to order his lawyers to lodge an appeal, which they did. At 3 a.m., a prison guard, checking his cell, hit the panic alarm when he saw a body hanging from the light fitting. Jack had hanged himself by his bootlaces. By the time he was cut down he was already dead.

And he died an innocent man. Because of the peculiarities of Austrian law, convicted criminals, who appeal against their sentences, are legally considered innocent until that appeal is heard. Perhaps Jack knew that when he took his own life. DNA testing is not infallible, there are too many human steps in the process and a lot of people wanted to see Jack Unterweger convicted. Was he the serial killer who wanted to be caught? Who knows? But his lawyer, Hans-Juergen Lehofer, was asked that very same question shortly after Jack's death. He said, 'The jury said he was guilty. And I believe it was a fair trial. Maybe, on the night he killed himself, he saw his victims coming at him. But now I've said too much.'

One thing was certain, DNA profiling was coming of age. There were now three techniques available to police forces across the world. The development of STRs had opened the door for the next revolution in the way crime was being fought. And it was just around the corner.

7

BIBLE JOHN

Tat-tat-tat. The ear-piercing sound of a pneumatic drill breaks the early morning silence of a Scottish cemetery. A handful of men stand around a headstone bearing the inscription 'Till He Come'. They watch grimly as the jackhammer bucks and twists against the hard frozen soil of a grave, until the sound changes and the drill finally breaks through into dry soft earth beneath. The machine is dragged out and men in blue boiler suits go in to finish off the job with shovels, hands and shaking heads. It is 1996. The graveyard is at the end of a track beside the village of Stonehouse, in Lanarkshire. Outside the gates, a group of psychics have gathered to watch and condemn. Beside them, the press folk talk quietly amongst themselves and take photographs.

Lime now lines the edge of the grave, spread liberally to minimise the chances of infection from the three bodies that still lie inside their crumbling caskets. Sixteen years is a long time for nature to do its work. The watchers are stamping their feet against the cold and steeling themselves for what they'll find. First the coffin at the top is exposed. Then, using a ladder to get into the eight-foot by six-foot hole, the two below are scraped free of soil. Despite the ravages of time, the three bodies have not decomposed into one mass. Police gently remove the remains of Elizabeth McInnes. She was ninety-one years old when she died in 1987. For the last seven years of her life, this strict, religious woman lived with the pain of knowing her own son, the son whose life had been tormented by whispers and rumours, had committed suicide in her loft. Now, in a final blasphemous indignity, as detectives pull his body from the quiet grave, she is lifted from the earth that covers them both and laid aside.

Within an hour, it is over. He has been transferred into a large coffin inside the white tent that shields the proceedings from the searching eyes outside. Two forensic scientists in green polythene aprons watch quietly as it is then placed in a police van and taken to the Glasgow City Mortuary. The next day, every newspaper in Scotland will carry a picture of the ghastly cortege and front-page headlines ask, 'Finally: Is This Bible John?'

It is the summer of 2002. Linda Coulter answers the door of her terraced villa in Glasgow's southside. Does she know the name of the narrow lane behind her house? No. She's pleasant but slightly suspicious of the reason for the question. 'Is it to do with the planning application?' she asks. No. 'Is it about Bible John?' she says. Yes. She smiles. 'We didn't realise the connection when we bought the house thirteen years ago. Obviously I had heard of him. I was brought up on these stories. We all were. Then I read somewhere what happened in the lane. But we're not superstitious.'

We go through the house, stop to greet her husband, David, then carry on up the flight of stairs to the garage at the rear and on out into the lane, Carmichael Lane – the place where the whole Bible John saga began so many years before. Linda, David and I stand in the midday gloom, staring at the recess that leads to the Coulter's garage just a few feet inside the narrow high-walled lane. It was on this spot, very early in the morning of Friday, 23 February 1968, that a young woman died a brutal and lonely death.

It was the swinging sixties – a time of flower power and sexual revolution when youngsters, the world over, seemed to be having a great time. Young Patricia Docker was about to join them. Her social life was beginning again. It was the year she moved back to Glasgow, the year she and her husband painfully split up. He stayed in the RAF. She took their son home to stay with her mum and dad in their flat in Langside. It could have been grim but it worked. Patricia was an auxiliary nurse. So was her mum. They both got part-time jobs at Mearnskirk Hospital, sharing the work and splitting the baby care. It took the pressure off everyone and meant Patricia could go out with her friends on occasion just like everyone else. She was only twenty-five, after all.

That Thursday night, she had put on her yellow wool dress, some nice strappy black shoes and slipped her grandmother's wedding ring on to her right hand. She came into the room, kissed her son night-night and told her mum she would probably go dancing in town –

most likely to the Majestic. Then she threw on her duffle coat and headed out the door into the cold February air.

Mattresses, bin bags and rubbish now line the lower end of Carmichael Lane. Weeds and grass poke through the cobbles. At parts it is almost impossible to pass without clambering over junk. Even in the daylight, the windows of the flats and houses bordering it seem far away, cut off by the high walls designed to give the householders privacy. It's even more secluded in the garage recess. It's, say, ten feet into the narrow lane and about five feet deep. A perfect place to hide unseen from the busy road. A perfect place to commit a murder.

Patricia Docker's body was found early in the morning – naked and very dead. She lay slumped across the cobbles not far from her own home, her face battered and bruised, her neck bearing the marks of the ligature that had been used to strangle her. Local residents were knocked up by the police and asked if they had heard anything. At a house nearby, a party was stopped and the occupants, journalists among them, were turned out into the street to answer questions from coppers who wanted to know who had come and gone. Nobody had heard or seen a thing. The details were entered into the police report. So was another minor but rather curious one. Patricia Docker had been menstruating. Nothing strange there. What had raised eyebrows was the fact that a used sanitary towel had been placed on her dead body.

Gradually, the police put together as complete a picture as they could of where Patricia had gone and who she had seen before she died. It was clear she had been dancing. But that wasn't much of a lead. So had up to 30,000 other people that night. It was not for nothing that Glasgow was known as the dancing capital of Britain. The whole city seemed to be obsessed with it. The Plaza, The Albert, The Locarno, The Dennistoun Palais, The Majestic are all names which provoke misty-eyed reminiscences from a whole generation of Scots. And there was The Barrowland Ballroom, of course. The Barrowland was just off Glasgow Cross, in the heart of the old city and a stone's throw from the rough and tough east end. Most nights of the week, hundreds of people made their way there to shimmy away under the glittering revolving mirror ball. It was hot and sweaty and exciting – especially on Thursday nights.

Thursday night was known as 'winching' or dating night. It was the night when only over twenty-fives were admitted, when married people slipped away from their partners at home, popped their wedding rings into their bags or pockets and put those vows on hold for an hour or two with a stranger. It was racy and sometimes a little bit hairy but, until 1968, it was usually pretty harmless fun. That was to change. Within a year, so many plain-clothes police officers from the city's 'Marine' station in Partick would be infiltrating the dancers that they would be dubbed the Partick Police Formation Dance Team by their colleagues. Still, when Patricia went to The Barrowland that night, there was no reason for any surveillance, no sign of the unsavoury reputation the dance hall was about to get.

She was supposed to have gone to The Majestic. At least that's where she told her parents she was headed. And maybe she did look in there and hear Dr Crock & His Crackpots belting out 'Obladee, Oblada, Life Goes On'. Maybe she went for a drink, as well, in one of the many heaving city centre pubs. There was no alcohol served in most of the dance halls so, if you weren't going to slip a half bottle of voddy into your handbag, then the smart thing to do was to have a couple of short ones on the way to the dancing. Nobody knows exactly where Patricia went but she definitely ended up in The Barrowland – of that there is no doubt. And, she definitely met someone there. And she definitely ended up four miles away from the dance hall, just round the corner from her parents' house. And, of course, she definitely ended up dead. That was about the long and the short of all the definites.

The police mounted a major murder investigation but Pat Docker's final hours disappeared into that swelling, moving mass of alcohol-fuelled amnesia that marks the start of the weekend in any British city. Back then, it wasn't a dance hall murder. It was just a murder and murders happen in cities. Senseless, stupid, sick murders which destroy the lives of parents and children and friends but barely make any impact on the consciousness of the rest of the population. People read about them in the newspapers, pause to try to comprehend the horror of them, then usually move on with their lives.

People like Jemima McDonald. Mima probably didn't give Pat's death a second thought when she headed off out to the dancing. It had been almost eighteen months since the murder anyway. Mima lived close to The Barrowland Ballroom, in Bridgeton, or 'Brigton', as it was known all over the city. It was a tough district in the east end, almost in the shadow of Celtic Park. It was only a hop and a skip from Mima's house to The Barrowland. So it was the logical place to go on that Saturday night out. That evening, Mima put on a black kimono and a white blouse and slipped a pair of cream sling-backs on her feet. Then, with her hair still in rollers – she'd take them out just before she went into the dance hall – she put a brown woollen coat over her shoulders and headed off for some fun. Her sister, Margaret, was going to look after her three kids.

Mima never returned. The next morning, when Margaret got up, there was no sign of her. But Margaret wasn't worried. Mima was thirty-two, a single mum and, occasionally, she stayed out all night. She was entitled to.

That Sunday was a scorcher of a day and all the local kids were out in the street, playing and getting up to the usual mischief. Margaret heard them talk of a body in one of the empty flats up the road. She just assumed it was part of a game. But, on the Monday morning, there was still no sign of Mima. And that was unusual. The children's chat about a body in the tenement was now worrying her. She went up to the tenement, in 23 Mackeith Street, herself, just to have a look and put her mind at rest.

Shock, horror, cold fear, incredible grief, who knows what went through Margaret's mind as she peered into the bed recess of an empty flat and saw the murdered body of her sister sprawled there. Mima McDonald had been strangled with her own tights and punched in the face, the police report noted. She was partially clothed and her black handbag containing her curlers and her scarf was missing. Oh, yes, and she had been menstruating.

There were two young women dead now. The shock waves were travelling faster. Mima was well known in The Barrowland – she was a local lassie and people must have noticed her. At the next dance, a police officer interrupted the music and stood on the stage to ask for anyone who had seen anything to come forward. He promised that the 'domestic difficulties' of patrons would be respected. The cops didn't want people hanging back for fear that their spouses would find out what they had been up to. They were willing to be very flexible to try to find out who was with Mima that night.

It worked to an extent. Witnesses did come forward. Slowly. Mima had been seen in London Road, she had been seen in a pub and she had been seen sitting on a settee with a man in The Barrowland. What's more, people said Mima had left the dance hall with him, around midnight. He was about six-foot-two tall, slim with reddish fair hair cut unfashionably short. He had also been wearing a suit and a white shirt. It was a good description. In floral, tie-dyed, long-haired, swinging '60s Glasgow, he should have stuck out like a sore thumb. He didn't. Sure, there had been enough sightings, to give a strong flavour of what the guy looked like. But not enough to lead the police straight to the killer.

Joe Beattie, one of Glasgow's tough old-school cops, was heading the police investigation. He suspected he may have had a double killer on his hands, there was the menstruating thing and both girls had been to The Barrowland. But he played it down. There really was nothing concrete. People talked, of course, and the newspapers speculated but the truth was nobody really knew.

The leads were, of course, much better in Mima's case than they had been in Pat Docker's. But the difficulty was in finding a way to jolt the public's minds into looking for this man. Beattie racked his brains on the best way to get the information out to the public. Then he and his colleagues had a brainwave. They took the various descriptions of the man and handed them over to Glasgow School of Art. Artist, Lennox Patterson, was asked to come up with a drawing of his face. It was to be Britain's first identikit picture and so lifelike it would eventually come to be known as the face that haunted a city.

The posters were put up in The Barrowland, they were carried in newspapers and they were plastered across the notice boards in police stations all over the country. It was an innovative step but it didn't solve the crime. Soon, too soon, the two killings, although unusual and even possibly linked, became submerged in the general hustle and bustle of city living. They were part of the city wallpaper. Life went on.

People carried on going to The Barrowland too. People like Helen Puttock. Two months later she didn't let the murders stop her from having a good night out. Helen's evening at 'the dancing' was to become, perhaps, one of the most notorious in British criminal history.

But it didn't start out any different from the others. In truth it didn't start out very well at all.

Helen had a blazing row with her husband, George, a soldier home on leave from Germany, about the fact she was going out. Eventually, he agreed to look after their two kids and let her go off out. After all, her sister, Jeannie, was going with her. He'd calmed down enough by the time the girls were leaving at 8.30 p.m. to give Helen thirty shillings for the taxi ride home.

It fell to Helen's mum, Jean, to remind the girls about the murders. She said they'd be better off staying at home, but Helen laughed, flashed her long nails and said, 'Can you imagine anyone trying anything on me.'

The girls had dolled themselves up. Helen was wearing her little black dress with the short sleeves and black high heels and she had slung an imitation fur over her shoulders. Jeannie wore a skirt, a blouse and a dark green coat with a fake sheepskin collar. Then they left the flat in Scotstoun, grabbed a bus heading down Dumbarton Road and went straight to Glasgow Cross. By 9 p.m., they were in the Trader's Tavern on Kent Street, getting a couple of whiskies down them with their pals. They walked around the corner to The Barrowland just before pub closing time at 10 p.m.

Thursday night – Palais Night. Murders or no murders they still came from all over, jostling and pushing to pay their four shillings at the door and get in to the excitement, to the heat, the noise and the thrill. Helen and Jeannie were no different. They were up for a good night out. Within minutes Jeannie was dancing. A man called John asked her on to the floor. She could see immediately that he was a good dancer. He could trip the light fantastic, cracking out foxtrots and waltzes with a practised ease. As he danced, he told her he was from Castlemilk, the large housing estate on the city's southside, dubbed by local wags the Chateau du Lait. 'Probably married,' Jeannie thought. He wasn't really her type but, boy, could he move. They shimmied around the floor, Castlemilk John chatting, Jeannie casting an eye over the crowd gathered at the edge. During one gyration she spotted a tall good-looking guy leaning against a pillar on the edge of the dance floor. He looked interesting. The next time she saw him, he was asking her pretty sister, Helen, to dance.

Helen's partner was no great shakes at the jiggin', Jeannie thought, but her sister clearly liked him. She brought him over to meet Jeannie and Castlemilk John later on. He was introduced as another John. They had a laugh about that, the four of them. There were always plenty of 'Johns' at The Barrowland on a Thursday night. He was definitely a cut above the rest of the crowd though, Jeannie thought.

As the evening wore on he definitely made an impression. He was so polite. Holding the chair for Jeannie and Helen when they went to sit down, avoiding the use of any swears in his conversation, just a cut above the rest. He had funny teeth right enough, Jeannie thought. The front two sort of overlapped. And he was neat with just a hint that he was a bit too neat. Kind of fussy neat. Not a man's neat. But it meant he was turned out well. He wore a well-cut brown suit, a crisp blue shirt and sported a nicely knotted tie with red stripes through it. On his feet, the girls noticed, he wore slightly odd, thin suede boots and, while they all talked, he kept fingering a badge on his lapel. His accent was west of Scotland, definitely Jeannie thought, and he was well spoken. In fact, he was a bit of all right.

Later, as the foursome left the dance hall, Helen's John would leap to Jeannie's defence when her money jammed in the cigarette machine, making yet another impression. The Barrowland was a tough place. The manager boasted a broken nose and a tasty scar on his cheek that made it pretty clear he was no shrinking violet. But John got stuck right into him and a bouncer who came over, about the cigarettes. He jabbed his finger in their chests with a cold, tough manner that implied he was a man used to being obeyed. And he got the money back.

Almost as soon as they left the dance hall, Castlemilk John left them at Glasgow Cross. He had to get his bus home, he said. But the other John wasn't going. He reminded the girls that the city was a dangerous place at night – there had been two murders and he gallantly offered to escort them home. The girls agreed and the trio jumped into a taxi for the twenty-minute journey back to Scotstoun. On the way, they chatted, although John seemed a bit cheesed off. Perhaps because Jeannie was still there. Three was always a crowd. He certainly wasn't very quick in getting his cigarettes out, she noticed, even though he obviously knew that Jeannie didn't have any. The girls had to tease them out of him and, after he'd reluctantly given them one each, he put them away without taking one himself.

But, as they wound their way through the dark city, he revealed a little bit about himself. He played golf, he told them. His cousin had had a hole in one. Oh, and he didn't approve of married women going out to the dancing. No problem there. Helen had told him her name was Gowan – her maiden name. Gradually, the conversation drifted towards that staple Glasgow subject – religion. 'Which team do you support?' Jeannie said, asking the city's favourite trick question. A rippling undercurrent of sectarian rivalry cuts right through Glasgow. So it was a loaded question. Those who answer 'Celtic' are identified as Catholics, dangerous in some quarters, those who say 'Rangers' are assumed to be Protestant, equally risky in other parts. But John gave the smart answer. He said he was an agnostic. 'What does that mean?' Jeannie asked. Then out of his mouth popped a long quote from the bible that, Jeannie would recall, included references to Moses and bulrushes. 'What was that about?' she thought to herself at the time.

That quote would later turn out to be from Exodus Chapter 2. It goes:

> And when she could no longer hide him, she took for him
> an ark of bulrushes, and daubed it with slime and with pitch,
> and put the child therein; and she laid *it* in the flags by the
> river's brinks.

It wasn't the first time John had spoken in a religious way. Earlier he'd described The Barrowland somewhat quaintly as a 'den of iniquity'.

As the taxi approached Helen's house, John insisted they drive past it and drop Jeannie off first. She suspected that her sister wanted to spend some time with her new friend and agreed. So they carried on to Yoker, a mile or two further away, where Jeannie got out and watched the taxi wheel round and head back to Earl Street where Helen lived. It was the last time she was ever to see her sister alive.

The next morning, one of Helen's neighbours, Archie MacIntyre, was out walking his black Labrador dog when he found the body of an attractive young brunette huddled face down against a drain pipe in the back courts of the tenements on Earl Street. It was Helen. Her face was bruised and battered, smears of blood trickled from her nose and mouth. Her jewellery had been torn off and her brown tights were ripped and torn. Those tights would eventually yank a man back from his grave but, at the time, they were merely seen as further proof that Helen had not succumbed easily.

Clothes were missing and money had been taken from her purse and a man's cufflink was found lying on the ground nearby. It was clear that a tremendous struggle had taken place, that Helen had fought for her life and nearly escaped by running up the nearby embankment. Grass and leaves were plastered across her body and there were signs that she had been dragged back across the lawn to where she had been killed. Her husband, George, alerted to the commotion by the ambulance arriving, came out and, in a state of shock, confirmed that it was his wife.

As the police gingerly examined the body, they found something which made their blood run cold. A used sanitary towel had been carefully placed under her left armpit. Helen, like the other two girls, had been menstruating.

The '60s were the heyday of Scottish journalism. Before the mass impact of television, the public bought newspapers in their millions to read on the trams, the buses and the trains as they travelled to work or home again. The *Daily Express* led the pack from its headquarters in Glasgow's Albion Street, the *Daily Record* was just beginning to develop into the giant it is today and Glasgow's own *Evening Times* was punching above its weight with a couple of hundred thousand copies sold every day. Glasgow was the centre of the Scottish newspaper world and reporters raced around the city in radio cars trying to out-scoop each other in the bid to land the headlines that would ensure their paper flew off the news-stands. Those were the days of the razor gangs, the killer hard man, Jimmy Boyle, the burglar tried for murder, Paddy Mehan, and scores more. There were shoot-outs in the streets, slashings up the alleyways and it was all recounted in breathless detail in the newspapers.

Life on the streets was echoed, after a fashion, in the hardened press pack where reporters sometimes slugged it out with each other for the best angle on a story or the chance to interview someone with a tale to tell. There were punch-ups, buy-ups and buy-outs but, above all, there was a staggeringly high level of professionalism and competitiveness.

The city had been a melting point for some of the biggest stories in the land during the previous decade. But nothing was hotter than the news that Helen Puttock had been murdered.

Three girls dead now. All young, all had been to The Barrowland and all had been menstruating. There was no denying a serial killer was on the loose anymore. The shock waves exploded over the city like a nuclear bomb.

At the time, John Quinn was a reporter on the *Evening Times*. He covered all the big, breaking, crime stories. He had been at the murder scenes of both Patricia Docker and Mima McDonald and had written the splashes that went with them. At sixty-five and retired, he recounts the details with a precision that proves they still live in his mind. 'There was a buzz about these first two killings. Police didn't say they were dealing with a serial killer but we did know that both girls had been menstruating. After that, every time there was a murder involving a girl, I was called in from home or pulled out of the High Court, to go and make sure it wasn't anything to do with The Barrowland killings. And there were other killings, of course, domestic stuff, things like that, but not related.'

The day Helen's body was found, Quinn was sent straight out to the murder scene in an *Evening Times* radio car. From there, he would dictate his copy over the airwaves to the copy-takers or typists, sitting in the paper's office. While he spoke, detectives were interviewing Jeannie. They listened with barely concealed excitement as the distraught woman told them detail after detail about the man who had spent the evening with her sister. And she was sharp, she remembered a lot.

Quinn got the call to head back into town and go to CID headquarters in the Saltmarket where a press conference was going to be held by one of Glasgow's most senior policemen, Elphinstone Dalgeish. What Dalgiesh told him that day made headlines that reverberated around the city for years.

'He said,' John Quinn recalls, ' "The man we're looking for is thought to be called John. He may speak of a strict upbringing and a strict parental attitude to drink. He may also mention a religious background and may make references to the bible."' Make references to the Bible! John Quinn almost ran out of the CID rooms and into the radio car. He told his news editor and then said, 'Let's call him Bible John.' And so the story of the bogeyman who haunted a whole city was born. The *Evening Times* wasn't the only paper to go big on Helen's death. In the next day's *Daily Express*, the by-lines of twenty-three different reporters testified how seriously they had taken the killing. Other journals spoke of the 'Dance Hall Don Juan With Murder On His Mind'. But it was the *Evening Times*' nickname that stuck.

Breaks in the case came thick and fast. Passengers aboard a late night bus remembered a dishevelled man boarding, at around 2 a.m., very close to where Helen had died. He had a black eye and one shirtsleeve was tucked up into the arm of his jacket as though the cufflink was missing. The man got off at the junction of Dumbarton Road and Gray Street in the West End, closer to town.

One fly in the ointment was that Castlemilk John couldn't be traced. The police were desperate to find him because, like Jeannie, he had spent so much time in the killer's company. He chose to protect his marriage rather than help catch a serial killer.

But Jeannie turned out to have a most impressive memory. She recalled Bible John producing a pink card to show Helen. When Jeannie tried to have a closer look he'd stuffed it away again telling her not to be such a nosy parker. Based on her recollections, the police were absolutely confident they'd get their man. The artist's impression had been touched up, though it was already so good that, when it was first shown to Jeannie in full colour, she said, 'A shiver ran down my spine.'

The scale of the manhunt that followed was incredible. More than a hundred detectives took up to 50,000 statements. Army bases, naval ships and golf clubs were visited. Hundreds upon hundreds door-to-door enquiries took place. A Dutch psychic was even consulted and enquiries were made as far afield as Hong Kong and Zambia. In all, 1,000 suspects were interviewed. Of course, the dancing was never the same after the third murder. From then on, detectives were present at every dance in The Barrowland and the aforementioned Partick Police Formation Dance Team came in to being. Glasgow went Bible John mad. Everybody, it seemed, had a hunch just who the dance hall killer was. Neighbours told on neighbours, workmates on colleagues, friends on friends as the fear gripped the city. It got so intense that, at any one time, there were dozens of suspects being looked at by the police on a number of bases, ranging from where they had been on the night of the murder to just how closely they resembled the identikit of the killer. One unfortunate colleague of John Quinn's on the *Evening Times* bore such a startling resemblance that the police eventually had to issue him with a letter stating he was not the killer. It was the only way people would leave him alone in the street or in pubs.

In all, Jeannie attended an astonishing 300 identity parades. She stood discreetly outside factory gates, cinemas, dance halls and pubs usually in the company of Joe Beattie. 'I would have been sure if I had seen him,' she said recently, 'but I never did.'

Beattie was deeply impressed by Jeannie's recall and took her with him as a sort of Bible John radar. But he soon had his own feel for the man. He had a special set of dentures made up to look exactly like Bible John's unusual front teeth, so vividly described by Helen's sister. He took them with him everywhere he went. On identity parades the first thing he would look at was the suspect's mouth.

John Quinn was close to Beattie. So close that, when he was once racing to a shoot-out which was supposed to be taking place somewhere in the north of a city, Beattie, coming the other way in his car, slowed down, leant out the window and shouted across the exact address.

'Bible John got under the policeman's skin,' says Quinn. 'Joe Beattie told me that he was convinced that, if he had walked in a room and Bible John had been there, he would have known right away.' But Bible John never did walk in that room. Those passengers on the late bus into town were the last people ever to be able to say positively they had seen him. After that, he just vanished into the ether. The largest manhunt in Scottish criminal history had come to nothing.

Years later, in an interview with *The Herald*, Joe Beattie would look back wistfully at the one that got away. 'Sometimes,' he said, 'you get the ones you shouldn't get and you don't get the ones you should. This was one we should have got. We knew so much about him. There he was with his short haircut, his meticulous dress style and the patronising manner he had towards women. I guess he lived west of a line from Stirling to Lanark. He was either a serviceman or an ex-serviceman. That document that Jeannie never got to see – it could have been a military pass. Looking back, I would say that we should have done more in following up all the military connections, going to all the defence establishments. We just didn't have the manpower.'

Fast forward to over twenty-five years after the Bible John slayings. Glasgow Corporation Police Force has gone. Joe Beattie has retired. Helen Puttock's sister, Jeannie, lives in Ayrshire. Helen's husband, George, now lives in England. Alec Jeffreys has been knighted. Jim Weber's STR technique is gaining widespread acceptance. DNA profiling is becoming more widely available to the police in Britain. A memo has gone around the various divisions that make up Strathclyde Police Force. It says, 'In the light of recent advances in DNA technology, it would be advisable to look over crime scene samples from old cases to see whether they are suitable for testing.' There was no bigger crime, no greater mystery, than the Bible John killings. The case shot to the top of the list.

Police evidence rooms are dull places. Rows of boxes lie stacked on metal shelves slowly gathering dust. Inside them, lie files and productions, fragments of lives and deaths. They're kept, often, in case of re-trials or, more usually, when a crime has not been solved. The Bible John files were a bit out of the ordinary. True, plenty of dust had settled on them in the decades since the case had been quietly laid to rest. But there wasn't just one box or even two. There were dozens of them neatly stacked in Partick Police Station. When the order went out to start looking at them, box after box was brought down and unsealed for the first time in decades.

In one of them, lay what officers had been looking for – Helen Puttock's brown tights, neatly labelled and looking like they had been put away only yesterday. Forensics fairly quickly identified what looked like a semen stain upon them. It was dried, obviously, but very well preserved. It was subjected to a chemical washing, using a detergent, then gently soaked in another chemical to soften the tough outer casings of the cells of the semen. The DNA was found to be in good condition. There was no problem establishing a profile from it. The problem was trying to work out who had left the stain.

The machinery of law swung into action. One of the force's best officers, Detective Chief Inspector Jim McEwan, was put in charge of the inquiry. Two detective constables, William Lindsey and Brian

Hughes, were appointed to sift through the thousands of documents. Partick police station's crime analyst, Susan McHarg, was given all the old statements and asked to computerise them so they could be cross-referenced. Detectives, who had worked on the original case, were called up and asked for their thoughts.

It was an enormous job. It took hundreds of man- and woman-hours just to whittle the number of suspects down to a handful. From there, all the evidence was looked at afresh. One name jumped out again and again. It was decided to test him. There was only one slight problem. He was dead.

His name was John Irvine McInnes and he had always been a suspect. Right from the start, people in his hometown of Stonehouse had had their suspicions about him. Maybe it was his womanising, maybe it was because he had been in the Scots Guards, maybe it was because he looked so like the photo-fit of the killer, maybe it was just because he had been brought up in the strict Brethren religion. Probably it was a combination of all these things. He had been interviewed at the time of the original inquiry. The phones from Lanarkshire went red hot as soon as the photo-fit was published. It seemed, in that old police cliché, that even the dogs in the streets were howling his name. He had been taken to a line-up. In fact, looking back, police realised it was the first line-up held after Helen Puttock's murder. Her sister, Jeannie, had been brought along and had looked into his face. She'd looked at it for a good few seconds. She said it wasn't him. But she could have been in shock. It could have been too soon.

Certainly, the more the police looked at his old files in 1996, the more things seemed to slip into place. John McInnes had gone to The Barrowland. He did wear a regimental tie on occasion and weren't the Scots Guards supposed to be a bit of an arrogant lot? Confident – the way Bible John had been that night in The Barrowland when he had argued with the manager over Jeannie's cigarette machine money. Then there were Bible John's quotations and his attitude to married women and that stuff about dens of iniquity. If that wasn't trademark Brethren behaviour what was? And John McInnes had been brought up in the Brethren faith. His mother Elizabeth had made sure her kids were God-fearing in the old-fashioned way. She pushed them to get the best out of them – mothered them a bit too much, some said. And

John McInnes was neat, liked his clothes smart and well turned out. He was a bit of a mummy's boy. Like Bible John. However, old Mrs McInnes had been disappointed in many ways. Her son had also turned out to be a drinker and a thief. He had a police record.

But there was another thing, a link that made McInnes look good for the murders. Something the original detectives hadn't been aware of. Something that could solve one of the many mysteries about Bible John's last night of murder. It had emerged that John McInnes had an aunt and uncle who lived in Berkeley Street in Glasgow's west end. That was just around the corner from the spot where the man who was seen boarding that late night bus got off. Was it possible that John McInnes had been the killer and he'd coolly gone up to his elderly relatives flat to clean up after killing Helen?

The answer to all these questions lay in that stone cold grave in the cemetery in Stonehouse. For it seemed that McInnes had really done nothing concrete in his later life to give the game away. There were no more murders and McInnes had not been in real serious trouble. Not much was known about him after he was excluded from the police inquiry. He had been thirty-one at the time, married and with children. Somewhere along the line his wife left him and he came back to Stonehouse to live with his mother. He took to drink and gambled. People said he had a short temper and was prone to violence. In fact, there wasn't anything in the profile of Bible John that people didn't finally associate with John Irvine McInnes. That may have been the reason he had committed suicide.

So his body was disinterred and brought to Glasgow. One of the first things they did was to open his mouth to see if his teeth matched those that Jeannie remembered from Bible John. It turned out John McInnes didn't have any teeth. But that wasn't important. What was important was what was going on in the labs. It was the first time in the world a body had been disinterred and DNA tested as part of a murder enquiry. Nobody wanted to get it wrong.

McInnes's bones were scraped and pulverised and analysed until they produced a DNA profile. Fragments of his skin were also subjected to the scientists' chemicals and processed to produce a read-out. It took five months. During that time, the world waited. The newspapers speculated.

Of course, it was all a foregone conclusion. The papers revealed McInnes's surviving family had already been tested. Swabs taken from their mouths had been subjected to DNA analysis and compared to that semen stain on Helen Puttock's tights. That's what had prompted the police to dig him up. After almost three decades, they predicted, the cops had finally got their man. Bible John had been unmasked.

Except he hadn't.

The DNA tests revealed only one thing. The sperm stain on the tights of Helen Puttock did not come from John Irvine McInnes. After decades of whispers, rumours and pointing fingers, the man who had taken his own life by severing an artery under his arm was cleared.

It was not the result anybody had expected. The sense of anti-climax that followed the confirmation of the negative test results was enormous. In the row that broke out immediately after, Strathclyde Police were heavily criticised for carrying out the exhumation when they had obviously just been groping around in the dark. McInnes's relatives spoke out bitterly and angrily about the horrific ordeal they had gone through. DNA was in the dock.

John Irvine McInnes was quietly laid to rest again above his mother. His grave was filled in. The tent was taken away. Everything was returned to the way it should have been.

To this day, Strathclyde Police will not comment publicly on the affair. Any enquiry is met with the answer that the Bible John murders are still an 'active case' and, therefore, not a subject for public discussion. The police are entitled to be prickly but the DNA tests didn't fail. Although the forensic labs were using only a fairly primitive test, it was sensitive enough to clear McInnes. Off the record, cops will say that nothing has been really proved or disproved. The tests just showed that the particular sample on Helen Puttock's tights didn't come from John McInnes. Who it belongs to nobody knows. When it was deposited there nobody really knows.

Maybe one day that profile will be matched up to someone living and finally the Bible John mystery will be solved. Only one thing is certain. John Irvine McInnes, at least, can rest secure in the knowledge that it won't be him.

8

IN COLD BLOOD

At the last estimate, there were 600 murderers living freely in Britain. Men, and maybe women, who have taken a life and got away with it. Men like Ian Lowther who brutally killed a woman, dumped her body in a river, watched as her husband was vilified and died as a result of wrongful suspicions and, yet, carried on with his own life. Lowther held down a job, raised a family, had mates, played darts in the pub, all not much more than a stone's throw from where he had raped and murdered. Nobody suspected a thing. But there is nothing unusual in that. We are brought up to believe that the unbearable burden of taking a human life will eventually weigh so heavily on murderers that they will begin to collapse. They'll make mistakes, have nightmares, give themselves away.

Unfortunately, this is nonsense. Living amongst us all are people who have committed the ultimate crime and, yet, they manage to carry on apparently unscathed. They are husbands, lovers, workmates, neighbours and, until very recently, they would have never, ever have been caught. Once the trail had gone cold – after the police had been forced, for economic reasons, to step down the hunt – they would have been free to continue their lives without having to look over their shoulders. For history shows that, up until the very end of the twentieth century, very few people were ever convicted of their crimes after the initial search had been abandoned.

Everyone has heard the popular myth that there is no such thing as the perfect murder. It is a fairytale that allows us to sleep at night and keeps crime writers in business. In fact, there is not one perfect murder – there are and there have been hundreds, probably thousands, of them. The murderers all rely on one thing to make their escape – time. Time covers tracks, deteriorates evidence, clouds memories and saps energy. As time passes, so does the chance of a person being caught –

time is not only the great healer, it is also the great deceiver.

And so it would have remained if it hadn't been for a breakthrough that took place in late 1995. What happened then was that the technique – which had been created by Professor Sir Alec Jeffreys and refined by Kary Mullis – was galvanised by Jim Weber's discovery. This was then perfected by a team of British scientists and turned into the greatest tool in the history of crime fighting. It is a weapon so potent that it could reach through the mists of time as though they weren't there and pluck cold killers from the hearts of their warm families. That breakthrough was the creation of a semi-automated system of DNA profiling. And it couldn't have come at a better time.

The truth was that, in the ten years or so since Alec Jeffreys had discovered DNA fingerprinting, everyone had been winging it. The original system was too greedy for DNA material, too slow, too complex and too expensive to be used regularly in the real world where evidence decayed and lawyers hit back. The struggle to speed things up and to deal with decaying samples had only succeeded in destroying the accuracy of the tests. They had become quicker and cheaper but they had nowhere near the discriminating power that Jeffreys' original had had. In fact, they were sometimes wildly inaccurate.

Astonishingly few people realised that. DNA profiling looked like an infallible science. Courts – at least those in Britain – treated it like an infallible science but it was nothing of the sort. Luckily, while the race was on to find a foolproof method, the public was largely ignorant of its failings. By the time they woke up to what had been going on, the next revolution was already well underway. By the skin of its teeth, DNA profiling would survive once again. But not before getting yet another wake-up call. In the UK, that call came from a journalist, named Fred Emery, who wrote an article in *The Guardian*, in late 1994, that was followed up by a television programme, which blew the myths out of the water.

'Unique, infallible, one hundred per cent. Gotcha,' Emery began, before pointing out that the scientific idol of the police and the public really had feet of clay. Emery had hit upon the simple but smart method of having his own DNA tested to prove the shortcomings. He had two samples of his own blood profiled and asked the scientists to tell him just how likely they both were to have come from him. The answer should have been a likelihood of billions-, zillions- even, -to-one. That's what everyone would have expected. Unfortunately, the truth was a lot more sobering. The best science could do was to say, with a certainty of one in 4,000, that Emery's blood had, in fact, come from him. One in 4,000! That meant that, in the average British city, one hundred people would share the same profile as Emery, in London, 1,200 people would share that profile and, in the whole of the UK, 12,000 people would have it. It was humiliating and frightening. It immediately sparked a wave of newspaper stories demanding to know how many innocent people had been falsely convicted under DNA evidence. The answer, of course, was probably quite a few. But, then, who could prove it?

Emery peeled away the myths surrounding DNA profiling until all he was left with was a seemingly rotten core. He pointed out, as the Americans had done years before, that the statistical basis of the calculations was a joke. A team of eminent scientists from London University's Queen Mary and Westfield College were wheeled out to put the fear of God in to anyone who had ever stood in a court and claimed billion-to-one chances of a false match. Dr David Balding pointed out that there had been crass errors in the way the statistics were multiplied together to give those staggering figures. Some of them, he said, should not be multiplied together at all.

The example given was a corker. Say scientists work out that the number of people with blonde hair in the population is one in ten. And say the number of people with blue eyes is one in ten. Then, by multiplying the two together, as some DNA experts did, you would have a one-in-a-hundred possibility of someone having blonde hair and blue eyes. That is quite clearly nonsense. Blond hair and blue eyes go together, as everybody knows. Therefore, the chances of someone having both were, in actual fact, still about one in ten. It was this method of multiplying the wrong things together to give astronomical results that was at the heart of the errors, they said. And woe betide anyone trying to argue against them in court. Of course, in real life, DNA profiling was done on junk DNA material with no obvious human attributes – not hair colour and so on. But the principle was the same. Emery then went on to an even greater problem – laboratory error. Again this had been highlighted years before, in the Castro case in the US, but the penny hadn't dropped in Britain. The horrors of band-shifting, where scientists often guessed whether something was a match or not, were spelt out to an incredulous public – as was the problem of poorly trained staff. DNA profiling was still a labour-intensive and relatively rare procedure but many police forces in Britain were beginning to have access to labs run under the auspices of the Association of Chief Police Officers or the Home Office or, in some cases, they used their forces' own forensic labs. And therein lay another problem. Mr Emery pointed out, they all used slightly different tests and had slightly different standards. The Home Office used one system, the Metropolitan Police another. Horrifyingly, the results obtained from both of them came out 'about the same'.

Much was also made of the fact that a number of people had successfully had convictions, based on DNA evidence, overturned in the British appeal courts. This was presented as further proof that the wheels were falling off the DNA wagon, though, in fact, judges backed the use of DNA evidence – they just threw out cases where it had not been presented properly. One of those cases was known in British legal parlance as Regina v Deen. Mr Deen had been convicted of rape on DNA evidence. He appealed, saying the prosecutor had misled the jury by muddling up the statistics. Basically, the prosecutor had confused the 'match probability' with the 'likelihood ratio' – a serious error. A retrial was ordered with the judges wittily dubbing such mistakes the 'prosecutor's fallacy'.

In another appeal case, Regina v Gordon, the appeal judges were told that the man had been convicted of rape after two different laboratories had prepared the DNA samples and a third had analysed them. They ruled that, although DNA evidence was generally good, the different standards in labs meant no one could be sure there actually was a match. Again they ordered a retrial. And in Regina v Lonsdale, yet another convicted rapist appealed against the DNA evidence, saying the police had used samples that had been taken from a crime he had been acquitted of to convict him of a later crime. They should have been destroyed, he insisted. The judges agreed and ordered another retrial.

Generally, though, the courts were pretty flexible when it came to taking samples, allowing the police great leeway. That was a sign of things to come. Nonetheless, many of these cases were reported in the press without great detail. It gave the impression that DNA was running into serious problems. When coupled with Fred Emery's warnings, it was pretty damning stuff. Behind the scenes, it seemed as though all was chaos.

The reality was that Fred Emery's warning had actually come a bit too late. It is not known exactly what test he underwent to get his own DNA profile but it is likely to have been a PCR-type test, known as DQ Alpha or Quad. If that is the case, he was given the wrong test. Both were rapid turnaround systems designed for poor quality samples. They only examined four loci and gave statistically very low results of the one-in-4,000s, etc. kind. It was specifically designed to handle degraded samples quickly. As Fred Emery was handing over fresh blood, and large dollops of it, there was no logical reason to use it. Any of the earlier, slower tests would have given much more accurate results because of the simple fact there was plenty of DNA material to test. If he had been tested using the very first system, the original DNA fingerprinting used by Alec Jeffreys, then the chances of the match being wrong could have gone into the billions. But, he wasn't and part of the reason for this was because the Home Office was then using DQ Alpha and Quad – albeit in conjunction with the older tests. It was a damning indictment if not quite accurate.

Because, behind the scenes, Britain was steaming full-speed ahead into a secret and revolutionary new system. Even as Emery's article hit the news-stands, scientists at the Home Office were finalising work on a profiling system based on Jim Weber's short tandem repeats. Short tandem repeats had already been successfully used all over the world – in the aftermath of the Gulf War, in Austria, in identifying what might have been Mengele's remains – but they were not mainstream yet. The reason for this was that scientists were racing to find the best loci, or points on the human chromosome, to sample. In Birmingham, a number of Home Office scientists, including Colin Kimpton and Peter Gill, were finalising the selection of six loci which would become the holy grail of DNA testing for police forces across the world. It was to be called Second Generation Multiplex or SGM. A year or so before, Gill, Kimpton and a number of others had come up with the world's first forensic multiplex system but it only had a one-in-10,000 accuracy at best and was never used in court cases on its own.) SGM was a whole new ball game. It was going to be a sensation. Six loci, known to the scientists as D21S11, D181S51, HUMTH01, HUMVWFA31/A, HUMFIBRA, D8S1179, plus one marker to determine sex, would be examined simultaneously. It was called multiplexing because a whole lot of steps, that had had to be done separately before, could now be carried out at the same time in one test tube. In addition, the slow process of blotting and electrolysing things would be replaced by a much faster fluorescent system. The results would be in the region of one-in-50-million accuracy. Not only that, the tests would be fast, accurate, semi-automated and available to every police force in the country. The tests would be the backbone of the world's first National DNA Database. This was the start of a serious corporate-style approach to the field and it signified the end of the days of great individual breakthroughs. Looking back, Dr Gill, still a consultant to the Forensic Science Service (FSS), remem-bers it as the end of a long process of research rather than a Jeffreys-style Eureka moment. 'We had to carry out an extensive validation study to demonstrate robustness,' he says. 'These things take time – we don't have religious moments as such.'

The world's first National DNA Database was not set up in a heavily guarded fortress but in a drab, totally anonymous building in the Midlands. Why the FSS chose the Markets district of Birmingham is anybody's guess. Perhaps, back in the early '90s, there was no real understanding of how potent what they were working on was going to be or how priceless the information they were slowly beginning to gather would become. Whatever the reason, that is where the database came to be housed. Within a very short time, the information held there would become priceless. Soon, behind its smoked glass windows, buried in its basements, with racks upon racks of industrial freezers, the material to solve murders and other major crimes would become available in a computerised instant.

By 1995, two decisions had been made by the government. The first was that, with SGM, they had a system that could be semi-automated and, unlike its predecessors, would provide fast accurate DNA results from crime scenes. Secondly, they weren't going to waste those results any more. Although there had been previous databases, they were patchy and not national. Now samples taken from crime scenes and from suspects would go on to a computerised database and be kept there to be automatically catalogued and endlessly cross-referenced, as every new crime was committed. It was going to be a sensational tool. To make it work, on 10 April 1995, the government changed the law to allow the police to take DNA samples – usually by doing mouth swabs – from every person in the country charged (not convicted) with a crime. A similar law was passed in Scotland.

Some weeks later, Don Dovaston, Assistant Chief Constable of Derbyshire police, secured his little place in history when he revealed a warrant had been issued for the arrest of a man in connection with a burglary in the area. Blood, found at the scene of the crime, had been sent to the National DNA Database where the computers flashed up a match to a mouth swab taken from a suspect in another case a few months before. The man was arrested shortly afterwards. Neither his name, nor the outcome of the case is recorded, probably because, by the time he got to court, other suspects had already been convicted.

Home Secretary, Michael Howard, issued a statement saying, 'My message to the criminal is simple – "DNA can catch you". Criminals must realise that the chances of getting caught are increasing all the time.' He was right. In the first three years, the database would process a staggering 200,000 samples and match 8,055 crime-scene samples to criminals. It was a revolution in policing and the rest of the world watched in awe. Not everyone was convinced though. The civil rights group, Liberty, warned, 'Many scientists are expressing concerns about the foolproofness of DNA profiles. We are worried that errors – especially human ones – could lead to the wrong people being arrested.' Funnily enough, they were right too – though it wouldn't be human error that caused the catastrophe.

Police forces around Britain were soon caught up with this remarkable new tool that had suddenly appeared on their doorstep. In return for a fee to use the database, they could dispense with hours of detective work. It went like a dream. Every force in the country was soon able to point to at least one major crime – murder or rape perhaps – that had been solved when the fax machine in the office starting humming and a piece of paper spewed out with the message from the National DNA Database that there was a match, or hit, from one of their crime-scene samples and a name on the database.

The case of Emily Mutch in Glasgow was just one of them. The murder of this frail old woman shocked a city that was inured to violence and crime and was known around the UK for its warm, friendly but tough people. The district of Garnethill is a melting pot in the centre of the city – home to the internationally famous Glasgow School of Art, sections of the city's Chinese community, immigrants, students and a few old stagers who were born and brought up in the area. Emily Mutch was one of that final category. On 4 July 1996, she was seventy-seven-years-old, a little bit frail and suffering from arthritis. Her family and friends pitched in to help her get the shopping, do the chores, those sorts of things. Because of the arthritis in her hands, she rarely locked her front door. She had just celebrated her birthday when, one summer's night, she was dragged from her bed, brutally raped and then battered and stamped on in such a frenzied attack that she was virtually unrecognisable. The details of the crime were so shocking that the unknown perpetrator was dubbed the 'Beast of Garnethill' by the local newspapers.

Very quickly, a large number of police officers were drafted into the area in a bid to get to the killer and to reassure the terrified community that a murder of such ferocity would not go unpunished. But, despite the case becoming a sensation in the city and although a huge amount of information had been volunteered, the trail went cold. By the time the winter had set in, few people were in any doubt that frail old Emily Mutch's killer had probably managed to get away with it.

For Elizabeth Mackay, Mrs Mutch's niece, those were the hardest months. 'Basically, we were all in a daze,' she said. 'I can look back now over the things that we did as a family during that time and it seems unbelievable to me. We were wandering around in a trance, thinking that we were getting on with our lives when really nothing was sinking in apart from what was going on in the investigation. As time went on, you kept thinking, "They're never going to get this person." It was a thought that made me feel sick. You began to wonder if it was going to have to happen to somebody else before they caught him. It was horrific but you couldn't help thinking, if he did it again, he might leave more evidence and they would catch him.'

Although nobody knew it at the time, not even the police, Emily Mutch's killer had already been snared by the National DNA Database.

Scottish police forces had long had their own DNA testing centres but, when the National DNA Database went on line, they were given extra funding to have all swabs and samples logged there. One of those samples came from a petty crime carried out by landscaper and small-time criminal, Thomas Galloway. Galloway, forty-two, lived in Maryhill, in the west of the city, with his family. One December day, he got involved in a scuffle with a petrol station attendant and pulled a knife. He was charged with Scotland's most piddling crime – a breach of the peace. Galloway was routinely swabbed and his samples pro-cessed and sent to Birmingham. And there they lay on the DNA database until, a few weeks later, semen samples taken from Emily Mutch's home were sent down to be logged. There was an instant match.

Once again the fax machine, at Strathclyde's Pitt Street headquarters, started to whirr into life before printing out Galloway's name. Mrs Mutch's niece recalled the moment when the police came to tell her that there had been a DNA match. 'One Friday night, there was a knock on the door at about 10.30 p. m.,' she said. 'It was a detective inspector and he had a woman police officer with him. He just stood in the door and said, "We have got him." That was the first time I cried.'

In court, Galloway tried to claim temporary insanity and that the DNA match was merely a remarkable coincidence. For a man who already had a string of convictions and had spent years in prison, it was an unusually optimistic stance. But, when it emerged that he had apparently kept two souvenirs of Emily Mutch's murder, a trinket box and an ornamental fan, in his own home, the verdict was a foregone conclusion. It took sixty minutes for the jury to find him guilty of murder. Thomas Galloway was sentenced to life imprisonment with a recommendation by the judge that he serve no fewer than twenty years.

Galloway fell foul of the oldest dictum in forensic science, 'Every contact leaves a trace'. This famous phrase was coined by Edmond Locard in 1920 in his book *L'enquète criminelle et les methodes scientifique*. It basically means that every action a criminal takes leaves some sort of clue, however tiny. In Locard's day, that would have been a fingerprint, maybe, or a fibre or even a footprint. Locard was thinking primarily of the fledgling science of fingerprinting which had the world enthralled at the turn of the century. He could never have envisaged the tiny almost invisible traces that police at the end of the twentieth century were now looking for. Apart from semen stains, blood and larger pieces of DNA material, collection techniques had improved to a level where it was possible to take a sample from a cigarette tip, from a fleck of dandruff, from the residue of breath in a balaclava, the criminal's favourite disguise.

With an army of police experts now entering crime scenes and painstakingly removing every conceivable piece of DNA material, a flood of information was gushing on to the Birmingham database. Even where there was no match with a known criminal, the perpetrators slowly began to realise that the only way to avoid being swabbed was never to commit another crime in their lives. It was a bridge too far for many of them.

So the National DNA Database worked and it worked phenomenally well. The Americans, in particular, watched enviously. If DNA testing had been done to varying standards in Britain before 1996, it was nothing compared to the fragmentation in the United States where a scattergun approach saw huge differences in the way states dealt with the science. In 1998, the FBI, following Britain's lead, set up their own national database to be called CODIS, the Combined DNA Indexed System. Because of civil liberty concerns, samples would never be taken as freely as they were in Britain but the age of all-powerful, all-seeing national DNA databases had arrived.

One of the spin-offs in Britain was, of course, the huge re-examination of old cases that were taking place. Every police force in the country took down their old files, looked at the physical evidence and, where possible, sent off samples to be tested and compared against known profiles on the National Database. This was not a new phenomenon. Ever since the first introduction of DNA testing, way back in the '80s, the most serious cases had been periodically re-examined as every new DNA test came on tap. One sample that had been meticulously looked at was from a woman called Mary Gregson.

Mary Gregson's murder was one of the strangest and most baffling of modern times. The mystery began on a warm afternoon, late in August 1977, when thirty-nine-year-old Mary left the stone cottage she shared with her husband, Bill, and her young son and headed along the canal towpath. It was 5.20 p.m. and she should have arrived at the end of the towpath a few minutes later. There, she was due to meet up with her friend, Susan, so the pair could walk to their jobs as cleaners at Salts Textile Mill, near Shipley. That's what they usually did. But Susan waited and waited and Mary never appeared.

Early the next morning, her body was pulled out of the cold, dark waters of the River Aire. The pathologist's report revealed she had been brutally attacked, raped and then strangled. Tests were carried out on her clothing. In 1977, the best forensic tool available was blood group matching. But it was never very powerful. The blood group A results from Mary's body could have matched thousands of people, including, tragically as it turned out, her husband, Bill. The dark cloud of suspicion that fell across the small town had terrible consequences. More than 11,000 people were interviewed, including every one of the 800 construction workers employed on a new Inland Revenue office building nearby. It was fruitless.

As the days stretched out, gossips pointed the finger at Mary's husband, Bill. Naturally, he had been one of the first suspects and his blood group was the same as that extracted from the semen on her clothes. Bill made the usual public pleas for help. He appeared on television and in local newspapers, insisting the killer was local and would be caught, but people talked and he was shunned. Talk fuels suspicion in small towns and others became caught up in the rumours. The four sons of Marion Abbey, who lived in Shipley, were also suspects. She recalled being blanked by townsfolk and of her life becoming a 'living hell'. Looking back, she says, 'All my sons were questioned, my house was turned upside down and we were followed everywhere we went for ten days.'

In January 1978, Mary's murder enquiry was wound down. But the shadow of suspicion never lifted. Two years later, the body of Mary's husband, Bill, was found at the very spot where she had died. He had suffered a heart attack. It set tongues wagging once again.

A full ten years later, the first DNA profiling, using the cumbersome single-locus-probe system, became available. The West Yorkshire Murder Squad submitted samples from Mary's clothes for forensic evaluation. Unfortunately, the system was not sensitive enough to give a clear result. The samples were packed away for another eight years.

In 1995, with the introduction of the National DNA Database, things looked far more promising. Mary's samples were sent to Birmingham to be subjected to SGM testing. Unfortunately, the DNA material, taken from her body, had been heavily contaminated with chemicals from the factory where she worked so, once again, the tests were inconclusive. It looked like the end of the road for the Mary Gregson case.

But it was a rare failure in the seemingly endless list of successes being chalked up by the Birmingham team. As countries across the world scrambled to emulate Britain, all eyes were on the wonderful new system now working, like a good Swiss watch, in the heart of the Midlands. Endless teams of foreign observers flew in and flew out, to examine the new system, report back to their governments and start copying it for their own police forces. In the United States, CBS's evening news anchorman reported that the UK 'was scooping up DNA evidence by the barrel'. He went on to tell his millions of viewers that British police had, that week, raided the homes of 1,000 suspected burglars to get their DNA profiles on the database. Everything was going magnificently well. Then the train suddenly hit the buffers in a fashion n -one had really expected.

It was a two-bit case really – a nothing crime in the great scheme of things. If anything, it proved how widely DNA testing was now being used. After all, the system, that had originally been envisaged as a method of trapping murderers and rapists, was now regularly being used to solve burglaries. One of those was at a house in Bolton where officers noticed a telltale stain indicating that the burglar had cut himself on the window while getting in. Scene of crime officers were despatched to the house and they ran a quick test to see if the stain was, in fact, blood because so many things can look like dried blood. The wipe they used to check it turned the right colour and they carefully swabbed around the edge of the stain before sealing the sample in a test tube, labelling it and sending it on to the National DNA Database. It was pretty much an everyday occurrence. Even when the fax came whistling back from Birmingham, it was still pretty much of an everyday occurrence.

The database 'hit' was to a forty-nine-year-old man, named Raymond Easton, who lived 200 miles away in Swindon. Local officers were informed and, one April morning, the police turned up outside Easton's house. As his neighbours looked on in excitement and astonishment, Easton was escorted into the back of the police car and driven down to the local nick. He was held there and grilled for hours about the break-in before eventually being allowed to return to his wife, Lesley, and sixteen-year-old daughter, Xaena. It was because of a domestic incident involving Xaena that Easton had been swabbed three years ago. The results of that swab had lain on the database until the Bolton burglary had come through and the connection had been made.

But Easton, rather unusually for an alleged burglar, had two pretty good alibis. The first was that, on the day of the break-in, he had been at home looking after Xaena who was off school sick. It was a reasonable enough alibi but not the sort of thing the police could be blamed for ignoring. But it was the second alibi that was the crux of the problem. It was the second alibi that would cause astonishment when it emerged the police hadn't paid attention to it. It was the second alibi that proved how many people were now blindly following DNA results, regardless of what common sense told them. Easton's second alibi was that he suffered from advanced Parkinson's disease and could barely dress himself, let alone drive hundreds of miles in the dark of night, shin up a wall, break into a house and scarper with the goods.

That was the reason, of course, that the neighbours had gaped in open-mouthed astonishment at the sight of infirm, weak Easton being loaded into the back of a police car. 'What had he done?' they wondered. 'Swiped a charity box?' Now, something had happened to the brain of the average copper between the introduction of DNA testing and Easton's arrest. And that something was blind, slavish loyalty to the new science. How else could anyone explain police officers carrying out such a ludicrous arrest?

After Easton was allowed home on police bail, nothing happened for four months. Then a letter arrived. Was it an apology, an explanation, a pleading story of an embarrassing cock-up? It was none of these things. It was a letter saying Easton, the man with advanced Parkinson's disease, was being charged with the burglary. The prosecuting authorities had looked at the DNA match, seen the chances of it being wrong were thirty-seven-million-to-one and decided it must have been him. Of course, what nobody in the police or the prosecution service seemed to have considered was that there were over fifty million people living in Britain. Therefore, it was entirely possible, if slightly improbable, that two of them had the same DNA profile. For that, believe it or not, was exactly what had happened.

Easton's solicitor demanded a retest. It took six months before a more sophisticated version of SGM – a version that could test an extra four loci and was millions of times more accurate – could be used on Easton's sample. The result was astonishing. It absolutely cleared him. The impossible had just happened – a false match. Not that the authorities bothered to write to Easton and apologise. They just slunk into the corner and hoped the matter would go away. The FBI were told, at a secret top-level meeting, during which they called the implications 'mind blowing'. But nothing was made public in Britain. The gob-smacked Easton launched a legal action for damages and said, 'I was all for the DNA Database before this happened.'

But this was dynamite. Of the many pitfalls to have befallen DNA testing since its inception, this was by far the most serious. Theoretically, the convictions of 63,000 people were no longer safe. It was the nightmare scenario that had had scientists tossing and turning in their sleep ever since the database had been set up. Emilio Viano, a law professor at Washington University, would describe the development as a 'bombshell'. He added, 'I predict there will be an earthquake in the criminal justice system.' If so, it would humiliate the British – who were still the front-runners in world DNA databases – as well as provide endless publicity to civil rights campaigners and, basically, destroy the whole system. But, curiously, none of that happened. Once again, an incredible set of circumstances combined to let DNA off the hook.

Firstly, the Easton story didn't break until fully ten months after the mistake was made. That was a staggering delay in a country with a voracious and fearless press. Maybe this was because nobody believed him until the second test cleared him – maybe he just didn't tell anyone. But that same second test was also the thing that saved the Forensic Science Service's blushes. Because it was a new version of SGM called SGM Plus and all it did was look at ten different points on the chromosome rather than six but that upped the odds of a false match to the billions.

By the time the cat was out the bag, the authorities were able to say, 'We've solved the problem. We have this incredible new test in place.' With SGM Plus widely available, the rash of predicted appeals disappeared because convicted criminals could not say all DNA tests were flawed. If they wanted to prove their innocence, they had to be retested under the new system. Not many volunteered and the whole thing blew over.

The Forensic Science Service had not covered themselves in glory during the affair. In fact, they never publicly admitted the error had happened. The story only became known when it leaked from the US end. If it was a deliberate strategy to delay the bombshell news until a new test had been developed, it worked like a dream. If it wasn't, then Lady Luck had smiled on the fledgling forensic science once again.

The new SGM Plus system was good – very good – and it had been relatively straightforward to implement. The test was exactly the same as the old one – as already noted, it just increased the number of loci or points examined and, therefore, massively increased accuracy. There was another new test waiting in the wings too. It was, yet again, another tweak of the main system and was called Low Copy Number. It was to be hailed as a magnificent scientific breakthrough when, in actual fact, it was probably the easiest step forward ever made in the field.

Creating the Low Copy Number test was pure and simple. Why no one had thought of it before was the amazing thing. Basically, all the scientists did was leave the samples in the PCR photocopier for a couple more cycles. This boosted the results dramatically and allowed them to capture profiles from even the smallest, most degraded crime-scene samples. But there were drawbacks and these would ensure that Low Copy Number was never any more than an additional weapon in the armoury.

Its main flaw was that the system not only dramatically boosted the profiles you were looking for it boosted everything else in there as well. Everything – all the background junk, the bacteria, anything, in fact, that had alighted on or grown from the genetic material since it was deposited – was intensified. It made analysis a little difficult – to say the least – but it did have some spectacular results. One of the first

– if not *the* first – was in the Mary Gregson case. At long last, more than twenty years after her murder, forensic scientists were able to create a DNA profile of the man that attacked her. Using semen samples in the underwear that had been fished from the river alongside her body, Valerie Ingram, a Forensic Science Service lab technician, carried out the tests on Mary's clothes.

Although there were only a couple of cells left in the semen sample, it was enough to give a result. 'What I saw during the testing was both shocking and exciting,' said Ms Ingram later. 'I realised the case could be activated with a strong chance of conviction.' There was now only a one-in-a-billion chance that the DNA profile they had recovered was not that of the murderer. It was immediately put on to the National Database to see if there was already a profile there that would match. There wasn't but it did prove, once and for all, that her husband, Bill – the man who had been found dead at the spot where she had been murdered all those years ago, the man who had been vilified in a whispering campaign – had been entirely innocent. It was too late to do him much good but it possibly provided some solace for his family.

Marion Abbey's four sons were cleared as well. Yet, another set of lives had been blighted by a random killer who, once again, seemed to have got off scot-free. but the police had no intention of giving up now. With echoes of the first ever DNA murder enquiry, they decided to mass-screen everyone who had lived in Shipley at the time of Mary's murder so long ago. It involved driving more than 20,000 miles to interview and swab men who had long since left the area. It was an exhausting job and they got through more than 500 swabs without having a sniff of the killer. But swab number 532 was different. As soon as it was processed, it registered a hit with the semen sample taken from Mary Gregson's clothes.

As dawn rose over the River Aire on the morning of 8 April 1999, a team of police officers knocked on the door of a forty-seven-year-old van driver, named Ian Lowther. Every officer present noticed that the front windows of his home overlooked the river that Mary had been found in. When Lowther swung the door open, it seemed to Detective Sergeant Gerry O'Shea as though he had waited, every day of the twenty-two years since Mary Gregson's death, expecting this moment to come. Lowther didn't ask why the police were there, he certainly didn't protest his innocence. He paused for a second before they slipped their handcuffs over his wrists, just to take his slippers off and lay them neatly, side-by-side at the door, and then he moved out with them into the cold. Ian Lowther, it transpired, had worked on that Inland Revenue building site beside the river all those years ago, when Mary had been killed. He was a married man with a young daughter. One day he drank seven pints of lager and, meeting Mary as she walked along the path, accosted her. When she told him to get lost, he exploded into a rage and raped and murdered her. Lowther eventually pled guilty. He was sentenced to life in prison.

Despite the close shave over Raymond Easton, the British government was still totally in love with DNA technology. They had another ace up their sleeves to increase the efficiency of the system. Once again they drafted a new law. This time, it not only allowed the police to take DNA samples from people charged with crimes, it allowed the database to keep those samples even though that person was later cleared of having anything to do with the crime.

The civil liberties implications were enormous. The Home Secretary said that innocent people had nothing to fear from their information being on the database. That was only true if you overlooked the catalogue of errors and mishaps that had accompanied the development of the new science. That was only true if you forgot that Raymond Easton and others like him – and there were others – ever existed. One voice, pointing out this was a very dangerous move, could be heard above all the others. It was the voice of Professor Sir Alec Jeffreys. Now an eminent geneticist, he called the police database 'seriously discriminatory' and said the only way to solve the problem of having a few innocent people mixed up with convicted criminals on the database was to test the whole population of the UK.

9

HANRATTY

Well, Mick, I am going to do my best to face the morning with courage and strength and I am sure God will give me the courage to do so. . . . I am going to ask you to do me a small favour, that is, I would like you to try and clear my name of this crime.
James Hanratty, 4 April 1962, Bedford Prison, England.

One hour after dictating this letter, James Hanratty was dead – hanged by the neck. But those two sentences – so casual, so relaxed, sounding as though the 25-year-old was popping out for a pint of milk, instead of walking along the corridor to have his arms pinioned behind his back and a noose placed around his neck – had a devastating potency. They would madden and obsess, inspire and, above all, accuse. They would settle on the British people like a fine indelible dust, a dirty stain, making James Hanratty's poignant, brave death unforgettable. And, of course, they would point a finger from beyond the grave – an unwavering, declaiming finger which would haunt British justice for more than a quarter of a century with two words, 'the shame'.

The shame was so great that only two more people would be executed for murder in Britain before the practice was abolished. A nation had had enough of cobbled together trials, grubby verdicts and lingering, nagging doubts. But, as the country moved on, it could never shake off the memory of Jimmy Hanratty's death. And, with every twist and turn of British justice, he would reappear. Into the chinks, the folds, the creases and the corners of the British legal system, his supporters would wriggle, holding up fresh evidence and new claims, refusing, simply obstinately refusing, to let his memory die. Until, thirty-five years after his death, science finally delivered a way of clearing him – a method so clean, so pure, it couldn't be tainted by dodgy policemen, strident victims or befuddled memories. And so poor long dead James Hanratty petitioned a court in his own name – implored it to set him free. And he left the grave, one final time, to give evidence on his own behalf – evidence that would finally release him.

The date was 23 August 1961. It was 6.30 a.m. Into the fresh sunshine of a crisp English morning walked young John Kerr, an eighteen-year-old Oxford undergraduate, doing a temporary job taking a traffic census on the A6 at a place called Dead Man's Hill. It was a nice, if solitary, way to spend a couple of summer weeks. But something had caught his eye up beside the lay-by ahead. As he strolled along, the strange shapes ahead of him, a few yards off the road, swam into focus. It was two people lying on their backs. A woman, closer to him, with her skirt riding up above her knees. A man behind – definitely a man. He was wearing trousers. John was almost upon them now and he could see blood on the woman. But she was looking at him, there was no noise, no crying, nothing. The scene was entirely peaceful. 'Are you alright?' John said. 'No,' she replied. 'I've been shot.'

And so began the story of the A6 killer, the story that would go down in the annals of crime history as one of the most perplexing ever encountered. John Kerr knelt down beside the injured woman and asked her what her name was. 'Valerie Storie,' was the reply. 'Please tell my parents,' she said. 'They'll be so worried.' The stunned young man asked what happened and, in breathless sentences, an extraordinary tale unfolded. Valerie Storie said, 'We were held up by a man with a gun who shot us. He said it was a .38. We picked him up about 9 to 9.30 in Slough. He has large staring eyes and light, fairish hair.' John motioned at the man lying prone behind her. 'Is he dead?' Valerie Storie replied, 'I think so.' There was, in fact, little doubt that Michael Gregsten was dead. He had been shot twice through the back of the head – the bullets exiting with tremendous impact through his face.

Despite the sense of alarm and concern that must have come over him, John Kerr wrote down what he had been told. He took a note of the description of the car, a grey Morris Minor, registration number 847 BHN and handed it over to the police when they arrived.

The ambulance crew, that rushed Valerie Storie to Bedford General Hospital, wondered if she would live. She had been shot five times with a .38 revolver. Incredibly, four of the bullets, which had entered her shoulder, her neck and her arm and had tumbled and spun their way through her body, had missed major organs. A fifth had severed her spinal cord. The surgeons saved her but they couldn't repair her spinal column. As she lay in hospital she was told she would remain paralysed from the waist down. She was twenty-two years old.

While Valerie Storie was being operated on, while doctors marvelled at the way she had survived the brutality of the shooting, while Michael Gregsten's wife was identifying his body on that hill, the police were already getting to work. Two officers, Detective Sergeant Rees and Woman Police Constable Rutland, were detailed to interview her as soon as she was strong enough to speak to them. Valerie's blood-stained clothes were also picked up by the nurses and handed over into police keeping to be used one day to help find out who had done this to her. One of those items of clothing – Exhibit 26 as it was to become known – would solve Michael Gregsten's murder. But there was a long road to be travelled before that would happen. A road littered with obstacles, twists and turns and not a few hidden pitfalls.

When Valerie Storie was able to talk, her story was extraordinary in the random way death and horror had stumbled into her life. In that summer of 1961, Valerie Storie, a quiet girl who had preferred to stay at home with her parents than go on to university, had been having an affair with a married man. The man was Gregsten, a thirty-six-year-old physicist at the Road Research laboratory in Slough. It wasn't a secretive thing. There were problems with Gregsten's marriage and he and Valerie, a laboratory assistant, had taken up together. On the evening of 22 August, she had cooked him tea at her parents' house and, at around 7.45 p.m., the two had set out in a borrowed car to try to come up with a route for a car rally, a sort of treasure hunt. On the way, they had a drink in the Station Inn at Taplow and left as it started to get dark. They didn't go very far. They stopped in the gateway of a nearby field and sat discussing the rally.

They had been there about thirty minutes when there was a tap on the window – sharp, insistent. The farmer? Michael Gregston wound his window down and met the barrel of a .38 revolver coming through the gap. A man said, 'This is a hold-up, I am a desperate man. I have been on the run for four months.' All Valerie Storie could see from the

147

passenger seat was the man's upper body – a very smart suit, a white shirt and a tie.

The couple were totally nonplussed. This was England, not America. These things didn't happen. Valerie said, 'Just put the window up. Don't let him in the car.' It was obviously someone fooling about, they realised. Except it wasn't. The gun was real. The man leaned in and took the ignition key from the car. As he swung himself through the back door, they could see his face was partially covered in a handkerchief. He told them to keep facing forwards adding, 'You'll be all right if you do as I tell you.'

The desperation in his soft voice was really frightening. 'I'm finking,' he said when they asked what he wanted. He took Valerie's handbag and Michael's wallet. Then he ordered Michael out of the car and said he was going to put him in the boot. Then he ordered him back in the car again. All the time he had his face covered. They begged him to take the money and go – to leave them. Escape. He'd be safe. Instead, he got back in the back seat of the car right behind Michael.

For two hours they sat there. During that dreadful time, the gunman told them he felt 'like a cowboy' with his cowboy's gun. But, he assured them he'd never shot anyone. He confided that he'd been sleeping rough for the past two nights and that he was starving. And he told them bits and pieces about his life in prison where he'd done serious time, 'done the lot' and he mentioned his horrible childhood, brought up on bread and water. All the time they were ordered to keep looking ahead, looking ahead into the pitch, terrifying dark.

Then, at the back of 11 o'clock, the man decided he wanted to eat and ordered Michael to drive. He told them he knew of a café where they could get something to eat – as though they weren't his prisoners at all and he wasn't some criminal maniac causing terror on a dark lonely night. But, all the time, his gun was pointed straight at Michael's back. For five hours, they were in the car with him, skirting around London and the outskirts of Slough. They stopped for petrol at one point, somewhere near London Airport. They were served by a man called Harold Hirons. He put two gallons in the car for the sum of nine shillings and nine pence. Then Hirons handed over the change from a ten-shilling note. He didn't notice the tension inside the vehicle. He didn't notice the gun and he certainly didn't notice that the couple in the front were absolutely petrified with fear.

So, their journey continued and, throughout the seemingly random drive, the couple looked desperately around for someone to help them. The streets were deserted. But the gunman seemed to know where he was going or, at least, where they were. At one point, which seemed to be in the Harrow area, he told Michael to 'be careful' as the car approached a corner. 'There's some roadworks round there,' he said. He was right.

Finally, the man started to say he was tired and wanted a 'kip'. He said it over and over again. 'Kip, kip, kip.' That was all he wanted now, they thought. Maybe their ordeal was over. He was obviously looking for somewhere to pull over. He spotted a lay-by on the A6 and they pulled in. Gregsten was told to turn the car around, to face the way they had come, and then park. The lights were all turned off and they sat together in the pitch dark. Again.

But he wasn't going anywhere. The gunman was going to take his rest in the car. He told the couple he would need to tie them up while he slept. But there was really nothing to use to bind their hands. He ordered Gregston out to the boot of the car with him and they found some cord. Together with the scientist's tie, the cord was used to bind Valerie Storie's arms and hands.

He then turned his attention to a duffel bag, containing washing, which was lying in the front of the car. 'Give me that bag up,' he said. As Michael Gregsten turned to hand it over the seats, the revolver went off. Boom. Boom. The car was full of smoke and the smell of cordite. Blood was pouring from the wounds in Gregsten's face where he had been shot at point blank range. Valerie Storie screamed, 'You've shot him, you bastard. Why?' The killer replied, 'He frightened me. He turned too quickly. I got frightened.'

Valerie begged him to get a doctor, to take Gregsten to a hospital – even if it was just to dump the injured and dying man there. 'Be quiet, will you? I am finking,' the gunman said. 'Give me a kiss,' he demanded. Sobbing, she refused. They were now facing each other. A car flashed by on the road, lighting his face for an instant, giving her a glimpse of the man who had been with them for hours now. She saw staring, icy eyes. After that, Valerie Storie was made to get into the back of the car – alongside the gunman. She was raped. As a final indignity, she was

149

told to drag her dead lover's body from the car. As she sat devastated on the grass, she said, 'Go away. Leave us.'

But the gunman hadn't finished with her yet. 'Be quiet,' he said, 'I'm finking.' – his favourite phrase. The thinking apparently over, he asked her how the gears worked on the car, how to switch the lights on and he even instructed her to start it for him. He stalled it. She started it again. He came over to where she stood and threatened to hit her. She felt for the money she'd hidden earlier when he first came into the car and held out a pound to him. He took it. She sat down on the grass and watched as he walked away from her. She watched as he turned, as he raised the gun and as he fired. The first bullet knocked her over. Two more thudded into the left-hand side of her body. She heard him stop and reload. Then he fired another two shots into her. Slowly the gunman walked over to her, kicked her a couple of times, to see if she was still alive, and then he turned and drove off. Valerie Storie was alive and she had remained conscious.

The hunt for the killer was enormous. It was played out before a national newspaper audience that gobbled up every detail of the grim case as though it had had no precedent. Clues came thick and fast. The gunman was no driver – that was obvious from the way he had questioned Valerie Storie about the basic techniques of getting the vehicle going. Anyone driving in a higgledy-piggledy manner wouldn't go unnoticed, the police thought. They were spot on. Two Londoners, John Skillett and his passenger, Edward Blackhall, saw a car being driven erratically in East London as they drove to work. Skillett followed it to give the driver a piece of his mind. As the car slowed to a stop at a roundabout leading to Gant Hill Station, he got a good look at him. Later, James Trower, also on his way to work at around 7 a.m., saw a suspicious Morris car turn into Avondale Crescent, Ilford, and stop. He clearly saw a driver with a dark jacket and a white shirt. And there was Doris Athoe, who lived at 6 Avondale Crescent, just around the corner from the tube station at Redbridge. She would tell police she had walked past a Morris car twice that morning around 7 a.m. It was, of course, the murder car, registration number 847 BHN.

Unfortunately it was clean as a whistle. There was no blood, no fibres, no nothing – surprising. The next day, Thursday 24 August, there was another discovery. Edwin Cooke, a cleaner at the bus garage on Rye Lane, New Cross, found a gun under the back seat of a number 36A bus. It was fully loaded, wrapped in a handkerchief and sitting beside it were five boxes of ammunition and some loose bullets. It was a .38 Enfield revolver – the murder weapon.

Then, as though the planets were aligning, a curious set of coincidences took place. A landlady had been assaulted as she showed a room to a man with brown hair. He tied her up and said he was the A6 killer. She screamed and he ran off. The police alerted landladies to be on the look out for someone who may have been behaving strangely since the murder. It led to a phone call from the Alexandra Court Hotel in London where one of their guests, a man called Durrant, had been behaving very strangely in the aftermath of the killing. He'd booked in the day after and not left his room for days. By the time the police arrived, he was long gone but a description was circulated and his details publicised. He came forward. His name was not Durrant but Peter Louis Alphon. The curious thing about Alphon was that, on the night of the murder, he said he had been staying in Maida Vale at a hotel called The Vienna. The number 36A bus, the one the gun had been found on, went down Sussex Gardens, very near the bottom of Sutherland Avenue in Maida Vale – very, very near to where the Vienna Hotel was located.

Things were just falling into place with incredible speed. No sooner had the Vienna Hotel registered on the police radar, than the manageress made a startling find. She was moving furniture in one of the rooms, Room 24 to be precise, when two spent cartridges cases fell out of a chair that was sitting in a little alcove in the room. They were tested and, lo and behold, they came from the gun used in the A6 murder. Astonishingly, the police now found that they had been led, by their interest in Alphon, from the dumped weapon on the bus, to the hotel, where the killer must have stayed, and on to the actual bullet cases. Then the results of the forensic tests on Valerie Storie's knickers came in. The Home Office scientists had managed to obtain a blood group from the semen stains found there. It was group O which was a different group from Gregsten's blood group and, therefore, extremely likely to be the blood group of the killer. Just under half the population has blood group O. It is around 40 per cent, in fact, but that 40 per cent included one Mr Alphon.

Naturally, Alphon had an alibi. He said he had been visiting his mother on the night of the murder and had returned to the hotel at midnight. The police questioned the hotel's night manager, Mr Nudds, who remembered Alphon well and said he hadn't returned until 2 a.m. Unfortunately, for Peter Alphon, his mother could not confirm his alibi. Incredibly, it looked like the police had their man. Or did they? The short answer was apparently not. Peter Alphon hadn't stayed in Room 24 but in Room 6. Of course, the fact that he wasn't registered for Room 24 didn't mean he was never in there.

Anyway, the police arranged an identity parade at Valerie Storie's bedside in Guy's Hospital on 24 September. It didn't go well. In fact it was a total disaster. She not only failed to pick out Alphon she picked out an entirely innocent man who had been brought in to make up the numbers. It wasn't over yet. Alphon also underwent another identity parade when Messers Blackhall, Trower and Harold Hirons, the petrol pump attendant, all also failed to pick him out. Stumped, the police released him.

Alphon clearly wasn't their killer but the trail had not gone entirely cold. There was another clue. According to the hotel register, Room 24, in the Vienna Hotel, had been occupied by one J Ryan in the week leading up to the murder. Mr Ryan gave his address as 72 Wood Lane, Kingsbury. When the police went around to the address to investigate, they discovered no J Ryan had ever stayed there. They issued a public appeal for information on the mystery man. It got a response. A man called Gerrard Leonard came forward and said that he had written a number of postcards for someone who he knew as J Ryan. The man was in Ireland, Leonard said, but one of the postcards was addressed to his mother, who peculiarly was not a Mrs Ryan but a Mrs Hanratty.

It didn't take long to establish that J Ryan was, in fact, one James Hanratty. In truth, people queued up to confirm that J Ryan was just one of the many aliases used by Mr Hanratty. But who was Hanratty? Like Peter Alphon, he inhabited the demimonde of petty criminals in London, moving from flophouse to flophouse. He had a criminal record. In fact, he had only been released from prison during the previous March. He had four convictions – all for crimes of dishonesty (housebreaking, burglary or larceny). In March 1958, he had been sentenced to three years in a youth prison. During the course of this sentence, he committed a number of serious disciplinary offences and attempted to escape several times. As a result of this, he was moved from a training prison to Manchester Prison and forfeited all his normal remission. When he was released, he went straight into a life of crime again, living entirely on the proceeds of housebreaking. He was so serious about his career of petty crime that he had had his hair dyed dark because he thought it would help him operate more effectively at night. But he had never been convicted of any offence involving violence or sex. In the course of their enquiries, the police discovered that people who knew him said he always behaved well with women – treated them properly.

Hanratty had gone to Ireland on 4 September, apparently on a housebreaking spree. As the police went off hotfoot in pursuit, they discovered he had stayed in O'Flynn's Hotel in Dublin, signing his name once again as 'J Ryan'. They then followed a cooling trail right through the country to Limerick and then on to Cork. But they didn't catch him. Hanratty had, by then, learned of their interest in him. He was to make the next move.

At midday on 6 October, the officer leading the case, a Detective Superintendent Acott, received a telephone call from a phone box in Soho. It was James Hanratty. He said, 'I want to tell you I did not do the A6 murder.' The next day, Hanratty rang again and mentioned going to the newspapers and also contacting his mother. A day later, there was another call from him. He said, 'This is Jimmy Ryan again. You will never guess where I am speaking from – Liverpool.' He went on to say that he had stayed at the Vienna Hotel but only on the night of 21 August, the night before the murder. On the day of the murder, Hanratty said he had an alibi – he had been in Liverpool.

Whatever James Hanratty thought he was up to by refusing to hand himself in, it was a pretty stupid plan. The whole country was looking for him. Newspapers carried his name, posters were up in police stations – it was only a matter of time. He was caught in Blackpool on 11 October. He initially gave a false name to a policeman, Peter Bates, but the game was up. The next day, he was brought to London and interviewed by Detective Superintendent Acott and a Detective Sergeant Oxford. But, instead of crumbling beneath the weight of evidence before him, as they hoped, he replied to their charges with startling confidence. 'I understand,' he said 'but, as I told you, I have got a perfect alibi for the murder. Fire away and ask me any questions you like. I will answer them and you will see I had nothing to do with the murder.'

The police couldn't help noticing something extremely strange about Hanratty that hinted that he wasn't perhaps the cunning master criminal they had been expecting. In an attempt to evade capture, he had had his already dyed hair, dyed and dyed again. As a result of over enthusiastic application of chemicals it had gone an extremely peculiar bright colour. It was the sort of colour that would stick out anywhere – and definitely not the sort of colour anybody, hoping to evade capture for the most notorious murder in the country, would have chosen.

It certainly stuck out like a sore thumb at Stoke Mandeville Hospital where Hanratty was whisked right away for an identity parade before Valerie Storie. Miss Storie would later agree that, compared to the others in the line-up, Hanratty's hair was 'like a carrot in a bunch of bananas'. But, of course, she didn't base her identification on the hair, which now bore no resemblance the hair she had seen so briefly in the car. No, her identification was based on something else. Still embarrassed by having picked out the wrong man in the line-up weeks before, she initially took her time at the parade. She asked to be wheeled up and down the line in her hospital bed. Then she asked for the witnesses to say the words 'Be quiet, will you? I'm thinking.' She was listening for the London accent and, in particular, the pronunciation of the word 'thinking' as 'finking'. After five minutes, she had made her mind up. She picked out James Hanratty. She would later say, 'I was absolutely certain as soon as I heard him speak.'

There was still Hanratty's alibi to be dealt with. On 13 October 1961, Hanratty's solicitor wrote to the police, detailing that alibi in full. It was explained that James Hanratty had gone to Liverpool on 22 August 1961, had then visited a sweet shop on Scotland Road and asked for directions to Carlton or Talbot Road and had stayed in Liverpool until 25 August. He also provided details of a visit to the cinema and a visit to New Brighton on the Wirral.

The wheels of justice were now spinning flat out. The stage was set for one of the most controversial British trials of the last century. It began at Bedford Assizes on 22 January 1962. It was to be the longest criminal trial in British history, with a total of eighty-three prosecution witnesses, fourteen defence witnesses and three people called to rebut alibi allegations. It lasted twenty-one days. James Hanratty gave evidence and so, tellingly, did Valerie Storie. She cut a poignant figure as she was carried into court on a stretcher and she delivered her evidence from a wheelchair. It was dramatic stuff. Paralysed, yet powerful, she was clear spoken and utterly convinced that the man sitting in the dock was the one who had murdered her lover and raped her. James Hanratty on the other hand came across as a spiv – cocky and confident with a hint of the night about him. And James Hanratty was not to be satisfied with damaging his chances though his demeanour in court alone. Oh, no. He decided to torpedo his own defence in a far more spectacular fashion.

A few days after the trial had started, his counsel revealed that Hanratty had changed his alibi. Sensationally, it was announced that he had not been in Liverpool, as he had originally stated. That, Mr Hanratty now admitted, had been a lie. Instead, he revealed, he had been in Rhyl in Wales. He had not wanted to admit it at the time because he was looking for a man he knew to fence a watch he had stolen. Trial watchers shook their heads. To change an alibi during a capital trial was tantamount to suicide unless there was some pretty powerful evidence to back it up. Mr Hanratty had better come up with some remarkable witnesses. He didn't. The landlady of Ingledene, the guesthouse he claimed to have roomed in, kind of testified that she remembered him. But it came across as though she wasn't one hundred per cent sure of the dates. It was all far from convincing.

Along with Valerie Storie's testimony, the alibi fiasco became a turning moment in the trial. Jimmy Hanratty might have been clinging on to fact that that there wasn't a shred of forensic evidence to link him directly to the murder but were the jurors? In the absence of hard evidence, they were being asked to decide whom they believed. Was it going to be the petty criminal and self-confessed liar? Or was it going to be the devastated victim who had to be carried into court?

On 17 Saturday February at 11.22 a.m., the jury retired to consider its verdict. Their heads were swimming. The judge, Mr Justice Gorman, had taken a staggering thirty hours, over three days, to complete his summing-up of the evidence. He had only finished it that morning. The tension in court was unbearable and was to get worse before James Hanratty would discover his fate.

The jury were far from confident. That was blindingly obvious. They had asked for a full transcript of the proceedings but the judge had refused. He did order that every one of the 136 exhibits be put in the jury room. Naturally, that included Exhibit 26 – although, as it had yielded little evidence, it was no more than a curiosity. After that was completed, the waiting crowds watched as the jurors' lunch, plates of cold ham and salad, were carried through the crowded streets and into the court. Six hours and thirty-six minutes later, James Hanratty was brought up from his cell into the court and told the jury was returning. It was a false alarm. They merely wanted to know the definition of 'reasonable doubt'. Hanratty was taken below for a few hours, only to be ordered back into the court at 7.30 p.m. This time, there was no jury there, merely the judge. Hanratty's counsel, Mr Michael Sherrard, seeing the jury was not present and suspecting it was another legal question, asked if his client could stay in his cell. 'I think it is causing him some distress, this constant . . .' But, before he could finish his sentence, the judge interrupted saying, 'I must have him here.' James Hanratty, a man awaiting the verdict in a capital trial, was brought into the dock to hear the judge read a note from the jury. It read, 'Is it possible for us to have some tea, please?'

Nonetheless, the delay was considered a good sign by Hanratty's family and his legal team. Counsel, Mr Sherrard, told Hanratty's brother, Michael, who had naturally sat anxiously through the trial, 'We've got this in the bag. They are not going to come back with a guilty verdict now.'

At 9.10 p.m., James Hanratty was brought into the dock again. This time the jury had definitely reached their verdict. The jury foreman stood up and, in answer to the question 'How do you find the accused on the charge of murder?', replied, 'Guilty, My Lord.' There were cries from the public gallery. 'The shock,' Michael Hanratty would later recall, 'it was just like hitting you with a sledge-hammer.'

James Hanratty was asked if he had anything to say. He hesitated, stumbled over his words and then said, 'I am innocent, My Lord, and I shall appeal.'

There was absolute silence in court. The judge bowed forward and the black cap, signalling the announcement of a death sentence, was draped over his white wig. Looking straight at the guilty man, he pronounced, 'James Hanratty, the sentence of this court is that you suffer death in the manner authorised by law and may God have mercy on your soul.'

Hanratty was taken down to the cells immediately after sentence was pronounced. The first person to speak to him was his counsel, Michael Sherrard. It was his duty to visit his client even though only minutes had elapsed since Hanratty had been condemned to death. Sherrard admitted years later, 'I didn't really know what I was going to say.' He found Hanratty handcuffed between two warders. But, before he could open his mouth, James Hanratty pushed his manacled hand into Sherrard's and said, 'You're not to upset yourself, Sir. We'll appeal.'

The appeal was held on 13 March. It centred on claims that the judge had failed, during his marathon summing-up, to put the defence case properly to the jury. No other evidence was brought forward. The appeal was rejected.

James Hanratty was taken from his cell to stand on the gallows' trapdoor on the morning of 4 April 1962. It was just seven weeks since he had been convicted but already there was enormous national unrest at the way he had been treated. There was no forensic evidence whatsoever linking him to the murder scene and no apparent motive – just a bizarre and, frankly, unbelievable set of circumstances which had led the police to their man. More than 90,000 people had signed a petition calling for clemency. It was ignored. He went to his death.

The trial may have been over but the holes were only now beginning to appear in the Crown's case. They would get wider and wider, eventually turning into chasms that the British reputation for fair play would, in the end, topple into. Soon it seemed everybody was talking about Hanratty and the unanswered questions. Questions like, 'What did Valerie Storie really see when the car lights shone on her attacker's face? Brown hair? Or was it light coloured?' John Kerr, the first person on the murder scene, stuck doggedly to his claim that Storie had originally told him the hair was not brown but light coloured. She denied point blank ever saying that and there was no doubt she was an exceptionally strong witness. But believing something was not necessarily the same as it being true.

Then there was the fact that much had been made during the trial of those roadworks that the murderer had known were coming up around the corner. The Crown had pointed out that the roadworks at Harrow were very close to where James Hanratty's parents lived. It was a pretty damning piece of evidence. The only problem was that, after the trial, it emerged that the roadworks weren't at Harrow at all but much further away – so far away that they were nowhere near Hanratty's parents' house.

And then there was the question of Valerie Storie's clear identification of James Hanratty in the hospital identity parade. That wasn't quite right either. Identity parades don't usually involve people speaking. Yet, all the line up had been asked to speak out without any precautions being taken to ensure it was fair. Had Jimmy Hanratty been the only real Londoner there? After all, thousands of people said 'fink' instead of 'think'. It might just have been his bad luck that the people who made up the rest of the parade were middle class or from different areas. There were any number of reasons why the identification parade was botched as lawyers stampeded to point out in later years. Valerie Storie, of course, clung to that identification. She was absolutely sure. But, then again, she had been absolutely sure a few weeks before when she had picked out an entirely innocent man in Peter Alphon's line-up.

As the months following Hanratty's execution ticked by, instead of fading away, the questions got stronger and stronger. Ms Storie answered them all with the answer, 'I was there.' Unfortunately, although most of the jury were not aware of it, being there was rarely any guarantee of accuracy. In 1902, sixty years before James Hanratty stood in the dock, a German professor had demolished the idea that nothing was better than a good strong eyewitness. Professor Von Liszt was lecturing a class at a university in Berlin one day when an extraordinarily bitter row broke out over religion. As the professor looked on, two students traded insults until one, shouting, 'You have insulted me!', drew a revolver from his robes and pointed it at his younger opponent. In front of a packed and stunned lecture theatre, the two men grappled with each other, struggling backwards and forwards until the frantic professor dived in to try to grab the gun. The weapon went off with an enormous bang. In the eerie silence that followed, it became apparent that, incredibly, the bullet had missed everyone. With order restored, the professor ordered the police to be called and instructed the other shaken students to prepare witness statements. Unbeknown to them, the whole thing was a set-up, a performance, to test how accurate witness statements really were. The results were incredible. In the words of one commentator at the time:

> Words were put into the mouths of men who had been
> silent spectators during the whole short episode; actions
> were attributed to the chief participants of which not the
> slightest trace existed; and essential parts of the tragic-comedy
> were completely eliminated from the memory of a number
> of witnesses.

Even the student with the best recollection got one quarter of the details wrong. Most got up to 80 per cent of what they had seen wrong. Dozens of other demonstrations have been carried out since – all with the same outcome. In the US in the '70s, NBC broadcast twelve long seconds of footage, showing a bag-snatching incident. The mugger ran straight at the camera, his face in absolutely clear view. The viewers were then shown a line-up and asked to pick out the culprit and call a hot line. The phones went red-hot with more than 2,100 calls being recorded before the switchboard could take no more. The results were sobering. More than 85 per cent of the callers picked the wrong man. A mere 14.1 per cent correctly identified the mugger. The scientific fact is that people get it wrong, get confused and hide it and, most frightening of all, subconsciously pick a face that looks familiar. It could be familiar for any reason – they may have passed the person in the street, seen someone like them at a party or just have selected someone because their features were an amalgam of other similar ones.

Given these well-known frailties in the human psyche, it was little wonder that people seriously questioned Valerie Storie's evidence. Nobody doubted, her sincerity. It was just her accuracy. And, it must be remembered that James Hanratty stuck out like a sore thumb at that identity parade because of his peculiar hair colour. What's more, Valerie

Storie was wheeled up and down the line-up three times and she asked its members to speak out twice – yes, twice – before she made her mind up. It was hardly powerful stuff. In the increasingly belligerent climate that existed following Hanratty's execution, it looked like an extremely feeble situation to base a hanging on.

But that was just the beginning. Everybody, it seemed, was now probing and picking at the case and it was coming apart at the seams. Nothing was quite the way it had appeared when James Hanratty had stood in the dock. Not even the police evidence was sound. Worse, it began to look as though the police had conspired to send an innocent man to the gallows. This staggering revelation started out as a whisper and gradually turned into a roar. The problem was that the police, it transpired, had not exactly been playing by the rules. In fact, Jimmy Hanratty's statement had been doctored by Detective Superintendent Acott. The policeman had actually inserted the word 'kip', used by the killer on many occasions, as Valerie Storie testified, into James Hanratty's police statement. At the time, this had been yet another nail in the young man's coffin. Much was made of the fact that it was a fairly unusual word and, when Hanratty apparently came out with it in the interview room, well, what can you say? Damning Electro-Static Detection Apparatus (ESDA) tests, a scientific method of checking whether words have been written into documents at a later date, would reveal, without doubt, that Hanratty had never used the word.

Then there was the not inconsiderable fact that the detective superintendent had failed to tell the defence that there had been witness sightings of the car on the night of the murder as far away as Derbyshire by no less than eleven different people at the same time. Incredibly, he had also failed to mention that Valerie Storie had originally told him her assailant's eyes were brown not the 'very large , pale blue, staring icy eyes' that so perfectly matched Hanratty's. Nor did he tell the defence that, a couple of days after the attack, she had told him her memory was 'fading'.

By now, the conviction of James Hanratty looked like an absolute joke to half the nation. There just seemed no end to the amount of material destroying the Crown's case. Even Hanratty's alibi, that ludicrous last minute alibi which he brought in to the trial in such a suicidal fashion, wasn't quite the half-hearted affair that the judge and jury had assumed. Awkwardly, it began to look true. Respected journalist, Paul Foot, travelled to Rhyl, went to Ingledene Guesthouse and was staggered by how much evidence there was that James Hanratty had stayed there on the night of the murder. He interviewed fourteen witnesses who said they had seen Hanratty with their own eyes. It kind of made a nonsense of the belief that he had been the killer at Dead Man's Hill so many hundreds of miles away.

The Hanratty family were the receptacle of all this information. When they sat down with their legal advisers and looked at all the faults in the case, they realised there were twenty-four separate incidences where evidence had been doctored or suppressed to secure a conviction. Geoffrey Binman, the Hanratty family's solicitor, said, 'If that material had been disclosed, James Hanratty would not have been convicted.' None of this was earth shattering to them. They had begun their efforts to have Jimmy cleared immediately after his death. His father, Michael, became something of a national institution, handing out leaflets and calling for an inquiry outside the House of Commons every day until his death nine years later in 1971. The pressure to correct the injustice was becoming enormous. Two journalists, Paul Foot and Bob Woffinden, wrote books on the case. John Lennon and Yoko Ono made a forty-minute documentary proclaiming his innocence and countless television programmes were made on long dead Jimmy Hanratty.

Not that the British authorities were willing to admit they could have made a mistake. Their first snub to the incredulous public was made just one year after James Hanratty's death. In July 1963, the MP, Fenner Brockway, submitted a dossier to the Home Office detailing all the reasons why the conviction had been wrong. On 2 August that year, an Early Day Motion was submitted to parliament calling for an inquiry. It was rejected by the Home Secretary. In 1967, *Panorama*, then a hugely influential documentary programme watched by millions, investigated the case calling it a miscarriage of justice. The Home Secretary appointed a senior police officer to investigate. On 1 July that year, the Home Secretary reported to the Commons that the conviction was safe but it wouldn't go away. In 1969, 1971 and 1972, James Hanratty's case was raised again in parliament. The government refused another inquiry.

161

In 1974, the Labour Home Secretary, Roy Jenkins, bowed to public pressure and appointed Queen's Counsel, Lewis Hawser, to reinvestigate the case. On 10 April, he reported back that case against James Hanratty was 'overwhelming'. Further calls were made in 1994 and ignored. In 1997, the British government, shuddering from the clamour over a number of miscarriages of justice, set up the independent Criminal Cases Review Commission (CCRC). Would James Hanratty finally get a real chance to be heard again? The answer was to be yes.

The CCRC inquiry was led by Bill Skitt, a former Chief Constable of Hertfordshire Police. He was given full access to all the files and evidence held on James Hanratty. The amount of material that had been stored for all those years was staggering. A large proportion of it had never been seen by the defence and some of it had not even been seen by the prosecution. James Hanratty's brother, Michael, then aged sixty, said, 'All this evidence has been locked away in Scotland Yard. They told us to come back for it in 100 years. We always knew there was something wrong. It is a disgrace.'

After reviewing the mountain of evidence that had accrued, the Commission was convinced that Hanratty was innocent. The end of the road finally seemed to be in sight for his family. The commission was to refer the matter for the Court of Appeal who would look at all the evidence again and finally give James Hanratty the trial he had deserved.

There was one last thing to do. For years, campaigners had been calling for DNA tests to be carried out on the evidence. It was the one thing that could categorically clear him without any arguments. There had been so many false dawns before – inquiries that were really just more of the same botch-up. Everyone wanted a definitive answer. The calls had always been rejected on the grounds that the samples taken from the crime scene were too degraded to produce meaningful results. But, among the boxes and boxes of material was, of course, Exhibit 26 – Valerie Storie's semen-stained underwear.

Suddenly, from not being able to carry out any DNA tests, three took place. The results were a bewildering mix of contradictions. Jimmy Hanratty was long dead, of course, and there was no DNA material available from him. So the Home Office approved an examination of a postcard he had mailed to his mother. This postcard had a stamp on it, which, it was assumed, Hanratty must have licked. The stamp was gingerly removed and DNA material removed from the amalgam of dried glue and saliva. The results appeared to clear Hanratty but they were not conclusive. The next two tests involved DNA material taken from James Hanratty's family, his mother and his brother. Again they were not conclusive.

By now, the Court of Appeal hearing into the Hanratty case was looming. The family knew that Jimmy Hanratty would be cleared this time. It was claimed that Bill Skitt, the man who had led the CCRC inquiry, had spoken to Hanratty's mother and told her that they had accepted that Jimmy was 'innocent'. Everybody just wanted the conviction overturned and a great wrong righted. It wouldn't bring James Hanratty back but it would lift a great stain from the nation's conscience. But the Home Office was dithering, delaying, mucking about. There was talk about digging James Hanratty's body up and carrying out tests on him. That would take months and months, not to mention the distress it would cause his family. It was quite clear that, as Britain moved into a new millennium, the sins of the last one were not going to be exposed without a struggle from the government. Then the Crown Office moved. They demanded the right to disinter Jimmy Hanratty. There was a new DNA technique available – mitochondrial DNA testing – and it should be used, the authorities said.

Although the technique had been around since 1994, it had only recently been refined by the FSS to make it more accurate. In essence, mitochondrial DNA is passed down through the female line of a family. It contains no trace of the father's DNA. Because it only forms a component of the larger DNA, called nuclear DNA, copies of it tend to survive even when single cells have broken down. Therefore, it is perfect for dealing with bodies that have been decaying in the ground for a long time.

The new technique that was on hand to use in the Hanratty case was called mitochondrial mini-sequencing and was five times more accurate than the previous method. However, there were still drawbacks. The first was that, because mitochondrial DNA is much shorter in length than that usually analysed, it doesn't contain a great deal of information. The second is that it did not work with the STR technique so it could not be compared with results on the National DNA Database. Despite these limitations, there was little doubt that the new technique would be extremely useful in examining the contents of Jimmy Hanratty's grave.

It would be the second time his body had been disturbed after death. In 1966, on 22 February, James Hanratty had been removed from a grave at Bedford Jail and reburied in a decent setting at Carpenders Park Lawn Cemetery in Hertfordshire. The family were not happy about more DNA tests. Knowing quite well that there was already enough evidence to free Jimmy a dozen times and that new tests would only stall everything, possibly for years, they demanded to know why it was necessary. Their QC, Michael Mansfield, argued in court that James Hanratty's case should be retried before the appeal court based on the evidence that was available at the time of his conviction. Why, go to all these lengths at the last minute when there was almost forty years' of evidence piled up outside the door simply crying out that the boy had been innocent. 'And what about the family?' he asked the judges. 'Do their feelings count for nothing?' There was a relative buried in the same plot as James Hanratty. 'Was she going to be disturbed too?' The whole thing would degenerate into a tawdry media circus. The appeal court was having none of it. They allowed the exhumation to take place. Crestfallen, the family were forced to accept yet another delay before they could establish James Hanratty's innocence.

And so, early one morning, as had become the fashion in such cases, Plot D 873 at Carpenders Park Lawn Cemetery was duly reopened. After all those decades underground, there was not a great deal of DNA material available from James Hanratty's remains but the Crown had anticipated that. It had been established that, between the layer of enamel on teeth and the central core, there was a rich source of DNA. Jimmy Hanratty's teeth were scraped and the material removed. In March 2001, it was revealed that, finally, the authorities had a result. It was a bombshell. After forty years, the mystery of the A6 murders had finally been solved. James Hanratty had done it.

When the incredible furore died down, it transpired that there had been a match between the semen samples found on Valerie Storie's underwear, Exhibit 26, and James Hanratty's DNA. The odds of it being wrong, the Forensic Science Service confirmed, were in the billions-to-one against.

It was such an extraordinary result that it left the Hanrattys and their supporters devastated. 'How,' Paul Foot asked, 'Could a man who was, without a shadow of a doubt, in Rhyl on the night of Michael Gregsten's murder, also be at Deadman's Hill?' It wasn't possible. Theories were advanced as to how Exhibit 26 could have been contaminated with James Hanratty's DNA. It was well known that PCR multiplied the tiniest fraction enormously. All it would need was a flake of James Hanratty's DNA to have fallen from one of his trial exhibits on to one of hers. During the DNA process it would swell to gigantic proportions and provide the link with the dead man. It was pointed out that Hanratty's clothes and Valerie Storie's clothes had been piled together on the production table at the trial. Then they'd been packed together in a box. There was also a mystery vial, which had become broken at some point, spilling its contents over Valerie Storie's clothes. Nobody was able to say what was in it. It could have caused cross-contamination. All these things were possible.

But there was one question nobody has been able to answer to this day. If James Hanratty did not commit the murder and rape and his DNA only came into contact with Exhibit 26, how come there was nobody else's DNA found on the knickers? If there was another man, the real killer and rapist, say, why is there no trace of his DNA on the knickers? It should have been there. But there has only ever been DNA belonging to James Hanratty and Valerie Storie on Exhibit 26.

And what of Valerie Storie? After all these years, she still lived in her parents' house, the same house in which she had prepared that final meal for Michael Gregsten. While the accusations had been flying and the temperature rising, she had kept her own counsel, refusing to give interviews, getting on with her own life. And, for a severely disabled woman, she led a pretty full life. She organised school reunions, became president of the local Women's Institute, met with friends and she never, ever talked about James Hanratty. Except for the day when the results of the DNA test confirmed he was the killer. Then she broke her silence to say she had never doubted it.

'Hanratty,' she added, 'was convicted in 1962 on the evidence before the court and the judge had done everything he could at the time to be fair to him.' She hadn't been in court to hear the original verdict but had been lying in her bed in at Stoke Mandeville Hospital. 'I heard it on the nine o'clock news,' she said. 'I remember saying, "Well, thank God, for that. It is all over." Had I known at that point there would still be these idiots, forty years later, saying it wasn't true . . .' And, with that, she slipped back into anonymity.

10

INNOCENCE

'Ladies and gentlemen, yesterday, when I was talking to you, all the lights went out. I don't know . . . Maybe that was a message. Today it rained. Maybe that was a message. Maybe the raindrops are the key issue but that's what you have to decide today.' And so the speech rambled on. This wasn't some drug-addled junkie addressing a minor court judge, on a piffling possession case, or some punch-drunk loser trying to explain his role in a tedious bar room brawl. These are the actual words of lawyer, Jose Luis Pena, summing up for the defence in a capital murder case. It got stranger. 'The system,' Pena added. 'Justice. I don't know. But that's what y'all are going to do.'

Sitting in the dock was his client, Davis Losada – on trial for his life and watching the jury listen to some of the more coherent points of his lawyer's defence argument. Mr Pena had been practising law for just seventeen months. Perhaps, that was some sort of excuse for the rambling incompetence of his speech. But it wouldn't really excuse the fact that he had also failed to cross-examine the key witness against his client properly. In fact, he had only asked him three questions. Well, not really three questions. It was the same question three times.

Some may think that an appallingly strategy for a defence lawyer to take when his client was facing the death penalty. Some may think that that sort of thing couldn't happen in a civilised country where people are considered innocent until found guilty and even those accused of murdering fifteen-year-old girls should be entitled to a decent defence team. Some may think that the man on the bench, Judge Darrell Hester, would have noticed that the defence had failed to deal properly with the one witness who could get their client executed. They would be wrong. Nobody questioned Mr Pena's strategy. Nobody even seemed bothered by the fact that Mr Pena had briefly also represented the very same prosecution witness that he was now so reluctant to grill. Nor were they bothered that he was deliberately not asking any hard questions so he would avoid going into areas he'd already discussed with that very same witness. It wasn't exactly a technique they taught at law school.

Of course, the judge may not have mentioned anything because he had appointed Mr Pena to the case in the first place. He may have believed, as Mr Pena later claimed, that the defence lawyer would 'roll over and play dead'. What the defendant, the thirty-two-year-old cook, known as Davis Losada, thought of the performance we'll never know because, on the basis of that performance, Davis Losada was convicted and sentenced to death. On 4 June 1997, at Huntsville Texas, he was strapped to an execution table, a needle was inserted in his arm and the customary question of whether he had any last words was put to him.

He did. 'If it matters to anyone,' he said. 'I did not kill Olga. Brian, thank you for caring. DeeDee, you have been a good sister to all of us. Anan – trust in God. I will always love you. Lynn, I will always love you. OK, Warden.' And with that the drugs began flowing to his heart. David Losada was pronounced dead at 7.30 p.m.

He had been right to preface his final words with the phrase 'if it matters to anyone' because, as he had no doubt worked out by that time, it didn't. It didn't matter to anybody. Because this was justice Texas style, justice in the United States of America in the closing years of the twentieth century, justice in the country which would proudly boast of leading the free world in protecting and respecting its citizens.

It wasn't pretty. Mr Losada may or may not have killed Olga Perales. We'll never know. We do know that his lawyer Mr Pena was disbarred some years later – not for criminal incompetence, not for failure to properly declare a conflict of interest. In fact it was nothing to do with Losada's trial. Pena was struck off for pocketing clients' money.

'I don't believe an innocent person has ever been put to death in the State of Texas,' so said George W Bush, then the Governor of Texas and, at the time of writing, the President of the United States of America. This astonishing statement was made in June 2000 in response to the uproar that followed a report by the independent Texas Defender Service and a separate investigation by the *Chicago Tribune*. They confirmed, as everyone already knew, that Losada was not alone in his experiences of the inadequacies of the Texas legal system. Texas has carried out more executions than any other state in the US. To date, during President Bush's tenure alone, 131 people were put to death. Few of them were textbook.

Here's a slice of American life. In forty of those cases, the defendant's lawyer either did not bother presenting any evidence whatsoever in their client's defence or called just one witness. This was not *LA Law*, or *Twelve Angry Men* or even *Ally McBeal*. No less than forty-three of those people, on trial for their lives and later executed, were represented by a lawyer who had been or would be disbarred, suspended or punished in some other way for their conduct.

Take the case of Willie Williams. Willie had plenty bad luck. Both his trial lawyers were useless. Joe F Cannon was notorious for sleeping through trials while Ronald Mock was to be disciplined three times and even jailed for incompetence. Cannon and Mock didn't bother properly reading a witness statement that could have changed the outcome of the trial. At the appeal, Cannon was joined by another lawyer who would later be diagnosed as mentally ill. In Wilson's case, they filed a three-page document saying there were no issues worth raising. Nothing. Williams was executed on 31 January 1995. Until Governor Bush began his campaign for the presidency, Williams was just another forgotten murderer. Cannon later died but Mock handled a further nineteen capital cases. Three were spared the needle but sixteen people were sentenced to death. He later said, 'I'm a good lawyer. It ain't bragging if you can do it.' Indeed.

And there is more. In twenty-three of the cases, and remember we are talking about a total of 131 executions, the testimony of jailhouse informants, people who claimed to have overheard something while sharing a cell or prison time with the defendants, played a significant role in their conviction. Look at David Wayne Spence's case. There was no physical evidence tying David Wayne Spence, a roofer, to a triple killing in Waco Texas. Even police doubted his guilt. But, when his case came to court, the holes in the prosecution's evidence had miraculously been filled by the testimonies of no less than seven jailhouse informants. The forty-year-old was convicted and sent to Death Row. Several of those snitches later admitted that the police had shown them pictures of the crime scene, autopsy photographs and other witness statements before they appeared in court – unorthodox to say the least. Court records also show that they were rewarded with special jail privileges (unlimited cigarettes, sexual visits) or, in some cases, reduced sentences. Although a number publicly confessed to what had happened, Spence was executed on 3 April 1997. His final words were, 'First of all, I want you to understand I speak the truth when I say I didn't kill anyone . . . Honestly, I have not killed anyone. I wish you could get the rage from your hearts and you could see the truth and get rid of the hatred . . . OK, now I'm finished.' Was he guilty or not? In the United States, where elected prosecutors boast of the number of death row notches on their bedposts, where they run election campaigns on the number of people they have executed, who knows?

Of course, it wasn't all down to two-bit lawyers and gung-ho police officers. The whole system appeared geared up for just one purpose – to keep the machinery of death working flat out. In the cases of twenty-nine of those people executed, the evidence of psychiatrists was crucial – psychiatrists like Dr James Grigson who testified in 166 capital cases in Texas. In 1995, the American Psychiatric Association expelled Grigson, known by then as Dr Death, 'for arriving at psychiatric diagnoses without first having examined the individuals in question'. This strange method of assessing a person's mental state would be laughable were the consequences not so terrible. Grigson was no fleeting expert witness in many of these cases. What he said was absolutely crucial to the outcome of the trials.

To obtain a death penalty verdict in the United States, it is necessary for the prosecution to establish that the accused is likely to be violent again in the future. Without expert testimony to back this up, the state cannot take a life. That's why Grigson was handy to have around. He was an expert at predicting that murderers were likely to strike again. He didn't even need to meet them. He made $150,000 dollars a year from court cases. But he wasn't the only psychiatrist in Texas death cases or in any one of a number of other states, who sealed a man's fate without ever having seen him.

And then there were the judges. In death-row travesties, in that state and many, many others, the root problem was local Texas judges appointing their cronies, or the incompetent, to defend the poorest men and women on the most serious of criminal charges. It was usually down to money. If you didn't have any, then why expect the state to shell it out on quality legal defence? When an attempt was made to stop this by taking the appointment of defence lawyers for the poor out of the judge's hands, there was an outcry. The judges saw it as a reduction of their power and lobbied the governor to put a stop to it. The governor, one George W Bush, complied and vetoed the bill that was going through the Texas State Legislature.

But not all lawyers are bad. Not even all American lawyers are bad. Two American lawyers in particular may, one day, be able to hold up their hands and say more lives have been saved by their efforts than by any other legal practitioners – perhaps in the history of the United States, perhaps in the history of the world. What they did was to take the new wave of DNA testing and use it to galvanise a magnificent volunteer legal effort that would reverberate around the country and eventually question the very nature of the death penalty. Eventually, for every overworked, useless lawyer cutting corners on capital cases in the states, a zealous, hard-working volunteer lawyer, or even a student, would spring up to pore over the mistakes and hold them up for the world to see.

They are the two men who ran rings around the prosecution in the Castro case – the two men who first showed that DNA could be beaten. Their names are, of course, Peter Neufeld and Barry Scheck. But, before they would wield DNA testing as the sword of truth in defence of the wrongly convicted, they would first make a name for themselves by doing the exact opposite. For a second historical time they would destroy the indestructable, disprove the unimpeachable, crush a DNA certainty.

The case involved a black former athlete and movie star named Orenthal James Simpson. It was to be spectacular.

To those used to the austere dignity of the British legal system, the apparent circus that surrounds high profile American cases can be bewildering. By the time OJ Simpson appeared on trial for the murder of his ex-wife Nicole and a twenty-five-year-old waiter, called Ronald Goldman (who had just happened to be returning the spectacles that Nicole Simpson's mother had left at a restaurant), few people in the States were not spellbound by the case. An estimated eighty million people had watched on television as OJ Simpson was chased along a freeway by police. He was apparently on the way to commit suicide at Nicole's graveyard and had left a note saying, 'Don't feel sorry for me. I've had a great life, great friends'. But he drove past the cemetery turn-off and kept going so, naturally, most people thought he was guilty of the two murders.

'If the dog could talk,' many people said, 'there would be no mystery'. The dog was Nicole Brown-Simpson's Akita guard dog, named Kato after Simpson's houseguest Brian Kato Kaelin. It had been discovered at the murder scene with blood all over its paws. It presumably saw its mistress having her throat slit, saw the same happening to Ron Goldman. Why didn't it defend her? It certainly led someone back to their pale bodies, lying there on Nicole's drive with their eyes open and their lips slightly parted, surrounded by pints of their own blood. The dog couldn't talk but the blood certainly could. The prosecution had carried out DNA testing on blood-stained items of clothing found at OJ's nearby home which certainly, scientifically anyway, said he had done it. The odds were in the billions, the evidence was 'overwhelming'. OJ was going down. Wasn't he? Maybe not. This was, after all, America. A country where no money gets you bad lawyers and plenty money gets you good ones.

The trial lasted six months. No less than ten jurors dropped out. The defence dream team cost $20,000 a day. Every minute was televised live. Personality photographers snapped away at OJ in court. Witnesses became personalities themselves. The lawyers became famous.

And, of course, two of those lawyers became very famous. It was their job to do the impossible – disprove the DNA evidence. They were past masters at it. Their names, as everyone would soon discover, were Peter Neufeld and Barry Scheck.

Although at least forty books have been written about it, getting a flavour of the madness that was the Simpson trial is difficult now that so many years have passed. It's fair to say the trial was more like a television show than a solemn court hearing. One day, for instance, thirteen of the seventeen jurors appeared in court wearing identical T-shirts advertising the pizza chain who'd supplied the free food they'd had the night before. Kato Kaelin took the witness stand wearing one of Charlie Sheen's jackets. After the celebrity photographer, Howard Bingham, had given evidence in court, the judge's secretary called him up to say the judge would like a signed copy of the book he had written on Muhammad Ali. Bingham obliged, turning up in court with a box of books to given out to the jury after the trial. He then had a private audience with the judge in his chambers. Only in America.

It gets more surreal. OJ Simpson's famous plea, that he was 'absolutely 100 per cent not guilty', had apparently been scripted by his lawyer, Johnnie Cochran. The catchy line 'if the glove don't fit, you must acquit', which was delivered to the jury in the defence's closing speech, was actually written by a real Hollywood scriptwriter. Amidst this frankly astonishing freak show, there was the DNA evidence and there was Messrs Scheck and Neufeld.

Oh, the DNA evidence was widely seen as the most boring and baffling part of the whole trial. For days, the nation slumped and slumbered in front of their television sets as the Los Angeles Police Department produced fact after fact, statistic after statistic, tying Simpson's blood to the crime scene. And they had done their homework. There was to be no rerun of the mistakes made in the Castro trial. This was 1994 and forensic DNA testing was still in its infancy but the prosecutors made sure that the tests had been carried out properly. Sure, it was boring but it was also damming. Or was it?

Seeing that it was difficult to destroy the credibility of the actual laboratory process, Scheck and Neufeld simply opened up a new method of attacking the infallible science. They said, 'Okay, it might be our client's blood that has been tested but how did it get into the crime scene?' The spectre of gross incompetence, planted evidence and racism suddenly loomed large over the trial, creating a cloud of doubt over the DNA results. The question of whether the tests were accurate no longer mattered. There was a new question, 'How did the DNA samples get into the crime scene?' It was a brilliant strategy and one that still has consequences in court cases today. It is now almost routine in rape cases, where there is DNA evidence that the accused had sex with their victim, to use exactly the same technique. Instead of questioning the accuracy of the DNA results, the accused will claim he had sex with the victim's consent, thereby, making the DNA results worthless.

OJ Simpson hadn't had sex with his ex-wife but his DNA was found at the crime scene. Was it planted there? The jury was persuaded so. One man in particular appreciated the efforts that were being made to get him off the hook – OJ Simpson. Barry Scheck was at one point described as Simpson's favourite lawyer and he had plenty of them. Such was the man's virtuoso performance that people were talking about him in the street. When Simpson was cleared, Scheck and Neufeld were tainted in the huge backlash that accompanied what was widely seen as an unjust verdict. But it wouldn't be long before they used DNA again – this time to rescue their reputations.

There's a routine in a prison death house – a noise and bustle that starts when an execution is scheduled. You can hear it in the condemned cell and feel it in the atmosphere. It starts with guards bringing in the paraphernalia of death, the bits and pieces that are needed to make an execution go smoothly – the sponges, the unctions and ointments, the salted water, maybe. Gradually, the traffic into the chamber becomes heavier, the noises become louder and then there is the banging and humming that all prisoners fear – the sound of switches being thrown and the electric chair being tested at full current. Crackle, zap, fizz, bubbling blood and frying flesh – deep down that's what the man in the condemned cell, with its dripping pipes and scuttling bugs, thinks he will hear next time that chair is prepared because he's going to bethe one sitting in it. Earl Washington Jr heard all these noises – the ones in his head too. He heard from the closest vantage point and he knew it was all being done for his benefit, for his execution just nine days later. 'I was afraid,' he said.

Every dog has its day, they say, and every policeman presumably has his. That day came for officers in Culpeper County, Virginia on 21 May 1983. Sitting before them was a young black man with a mental age of ten. He'd been drinking and got himself into a hell of a lot of trouble after hitting an elderly woman with a chair, stealing her pistol and then shooting his brother in the foot with it. Not that the man, Earl Washington, was proving any trouble for the police officers, from Culpeper County and Fauquier County, Virginia State, gathered around him. Whatever they said, he agreed with. Yep, he stole the gun, yep, he hit the woman and, yep, he shot his brother. It was quite frankly astonishing – even quite funny if you were of that mind-set. Then one of the policemen had a brainwave, the sort of hunch that detectives all over the world dream of. 'Earl,' he said, 'Did you do that break-in just down the road on Waterloo St?' 'Yes, Sir,' Earl replied. 'The one on

Washington Street?' 'Yes, Sir.' 'Did you rape that woman in town?' 'Yes, Sir.' Then Deputy Terry Schrum asked, 'Earl, DID YOU KILL THAT GIRL IN CULPEPER?' Earl sat quietly for five seconds, nodded his head and begun crying. Under further questioning, he furnished the police with a few more details. The woman he'd apparently murdered in Culpeper was black, short and had been on her own when he stabbed her twice.

It was some day for cleaning up crimes in Culpeper County. In the space of an hour or two, the detection rate had just gone through the roof. There may have been a bit of back-slapping going on amongst the police officers as they trooped out of the interview room and just a few wide smiles but it didn't last too long.

Disappointingly, but perhaps not too surprisingly to those with a modicum of intelligence, not even the Culpeper Police could manage to stick all those new crimes to Earl. In fact, in every crime where there had been a witness the charges were dropped against Earl, that simple young man with the IQ of 69. This was because of the slight technical hitch that, every time Earl was taken to a line-up, the witnesses said quite categorically, unequivocally, the cops had got the wrong guy.

There had been no witnesses to the murder of Rebecca Lynn Williams. She had been stabbed to death in her apartment a year ago. But the manner of her death should perhaps have alerted the Culpeper Police that Earl, in this case, as in the others, wasn't their man. For a start she had been raped and stabbed thirty-eight times, not twice as Earl had said. She wasn't short, but five-foot-eight tall, and she hadn't been in the apartment alone. He children were there. It took the police four goes before somehow, miraculously almost, Earl got his statement right. Then there was the problem of the apartment. Earl just couldn't identify it. And he was supposed to have been there that murderous day. Still, the Culpeper Police were nothing if not resourceful. They took him back to the apartment block three times in one afternoon and on the last visit an officer helpfully pointed Earl in the direction of the right door.

Before the trial, Washington's lawyer tried to persuade the judge just how easily ledEarle was by staging a little show. He told Earl that today was Earle's birthday. For a few minutes, Earle protested that it wasn't his birthday at all but soon he agreed with his lawyer and seemd convinced that it was, indeed, his birthday. It was a nice bit of court pantomime with a serious point. The judge wasn't impressed. Earl stood trial.

As he gave his final plea to the jury in Washington's defence, John W Scott Jnr, appearing in his first murder case, knew things weren't going well. He later recalled the sound of rustling papers, people whispering, others eating. All that was missing was some tumbleweed bouncing through the room and the sound of a bell tolling. After a mere fifty minutes of deliberation, the jury found Earl guilty. Then it took just another hour and a half for them to come up with the death penalty. Earl Washington cried.

On 16 August, a state car took Washington from the Mecklenburg Correctional Centre to await execution at the death house at Virginia State Penitentiary. He was only on Death Row for twenty months before he was transferred there. (Death row inmates were separated from those about to be executed to avoid the danger of riots.) There was no appeal hearing because the judge had refused to authorise funds to pay for a lawyer to represent Earl, which meant that this virtually illiterate, mentally retarded young man was totally on his own. Await-ing the inevitable. There was no attempt being made to stop it.

Then Earl got a little bit of luck. He had one friend on Death Row –a prisoner, named Joseph Giarratano, whom he had met on his first day. Earl couldn't read so Giarratano looked after his mail. One day, he opened a letter addressed to Earl. It was from the Virginia State Court saying a date had been set for Earl's execution. It looked like the end of the road. 'Picture yourself in this situation,' Giarratano told the *Virginian-Pilot*, 'you must file something with the court or be executed. But, before you can file, you must learn to read write, overcome your retardation, obtain your trial transcript, understand the science of law – understand civil procedure, constitutional law, criminal law and acquire the art of writing.' It wasn't going to happen.

But Garratano, who was himself in a perilous situation, did something that saved Washington's life. He begged a prison volunteer named Marie Deans to go to the death house and do something to help Washington. Deans met Earl in the 'Cooling Off Room' – so-called because it was where electrocuted bodies were brought to be cooled down and straightened out for burial. 'They were testing the electric chair,' she recalled. 'And we all knew it was happening'.

The problem for Giarratano and Deans was how to persuade a law firm to take on Earl's case, for nothing, only weeks before execution. But, as luck would have it, Giarratano's own civil case had been picked up by the National Association For the Advancement of Coloured People. And they had funded a New York law firm who sent a junior lawyer down to see him. The first words out of Giarratano's mouth, when that lawyer walked into his cell, were that Earl Washington was going to be executed in two weeks and, 'he has no lawyer.'

Eric Freedman, one of the bosses at law firm, Paul, Weiss, Rifkind and Garrison, agreed to take the case on and, over a single weekend, a staggering 1,200-page petition, presenting Washington's case, was put together. Nine days before the execution was due to take place, it was halted. It seemed as though Earl Washington was about to be saved but, in reality, he was just at the beginning of his journey.

The next two things that happened would, to the minds of most reasonable people, seem like more than enough to prove Washington's innocence. Firstly, as his new law team pored over what scant evidence there was from the original trial, they discovered something astonishing. Blood tests had been carried out on the semen left by Rebecca Lynn Williams' attacker. It showed the attacker had blood group A. Earl Washington's blood group is O. It couldn't have been Earl. It was something that should have been noticed by the trial lawyer. It wasn't. Perhaps the state of Virginia, which carried out the tests, might have mentioned it given that it was such an incredible piece of evidence indicating Earl's innocence. They didn't.

Not that it made any difference. On 23 December 1986, a state court refused a hearing and, on 26 February 1988, Virginia Supreme Court also shut the door in Earl Washington's face. When Earl's lawyers presented the staggering proof that he was innocent to the US District Court on 25 October 1989, they too upheld his sentence. The US Fourth Circuit Court of Appeals sent the case back for an evidentiary hearing on the claims that Earl's blood tests had not been presented to court because of legal incompetence. The district court rejected it again. On 17 September 1993, the Court of Appeal backed that decision although one judge, John D Butzner, said that Washington had been exonerated by the State's own crime lab. The other two judges didn't agree. His lawyers expected an imminent execution date to now be set.

Desperate now, Washington's lawyers turned to the experts in DNA, Barry Scheck and Peter Neufeld, and consulted them on taking tests. In 1992, Scheck and Neufeld had set up an organisation called the Innocence Project at the Benjamin N Cardozo School of Law in New York. Staffed by students, it existed solely to use post-conviction DNA testing to establish innocence. These were early days but it was to become an extremely influential organisation. They agreed to help Earl Washington Jr.

Tests were done on the semen sample left at the crime scene using what would now be considered a fairly primitive four-allele system that was probably DQ Alpha. It might have been primitive but it picked out the fact that at least one of the DNA traces did not belong to the victim or Earl Washington or her husband. In her dying statement, Rebecca Lynn Williams had told her husband and the police that she had been attacked by a lone black man. No one else. That wasn't Earl's DNA. He was an innocent man. Again.

Unfortunately not. Establishing innocence in the State of Virginia, after conviction, had been turned into a virtual impossibility. To anyone with a belief in justice, Virginia's twenty-one-day rule seems like one of the most incredibly unjust pieces of legislation ever passed. It states that new evidence can only be considered by an appeal court within twenty-one days of the original verdict being passed. It doesn't matter how strong the new evidence is. If it isn't produced within those three short weeks, it is deemed to be irrelevant. Earl's evidence had not been discovered within that timescale. He may well have been an innocent, but, to the State of Virginia, that was now irrelevant. To avoid confusion Virginia State Attorney General Mary Sue Terry helpfully clarified the situation by stating publicly, 'Innocence is irrelevant.' Earl had to die.

Earl's legal team, which by now had expanded dramatically, had no option but to petition the state's governor L Douglas Wilder for clemency. That petition was lodged on 20 December 1993. But, faced with overwhelming evidence that he was not the murderer, the governor's team did not cave in. Instead, they cobbled up a new theory. What if Earl Washington had had an accomplice and it was the accomplice's semen that had been identified in the DNA testing? This left Earl's team dumfounded. Rebecca Lynn Williams had told her husband and a police officer that there was just one single, lone, assailant. That was it. Surely the governor wasn't being serious? Unfortunately he was.

The governor ordered another DNA test on the semen. This was done in secret. Earl's team were not told of the results or even if the tests had been concluded. The only hope for Earl was that the governor, who was stepping down from office, would include Earl in the traditional list of pardons.

No one on Earl's team knew the results of that secret DNA testing. On 14 January 1994, as the clock ticked down the final minutes of the governor's last day, the situation looked hopeless. Suddenly a fax appeared in the office of Earl's lawyers offering clemency – of a sort. He had two hours to accept a life sentence in prison instead of the death penalty. Failure to agree would result in Earl Washington being executed for a crime very few people now believed he committed. Stuck between a rock and a hard place, Washington accepted. It was a bitter, immoral and unjust offer.

It would later emerge that the DNA tests, carried out for the governor and shown to him on 14 January, concluded that Earl Washington was 'eliminated' as the person whose sperm had been taken from the crime scene. He was not the murderer. That was little consolation for the man who was now destined to spend the rest of his life in prison for a crime he did not commit.

However, his case was not forgotten. A massive volunteer operation was now working for Earl Washington's release – including the combined efforts of the the Innocence Project. In all, more than $20m in volunteer legal time would be committed to the case – staggering when it is considered that a Virginia judge refused a few dollars to pay for representation at his appeal. It would take forever.

then, five years after Earl's death sentence had been cut to life imprisonment, the Virginia General Assembly was asked to drop the twenty-one-day rule and pave the way for him to have a new trial. They refused and, instead, extended the rule. But the Innocence Project was beginning to have major successes with other death-row prisoners and, on the back of that, journalists were encouraged to look at the scandal that was the Earl Washington case. Huge newspaper pressure was brought to bear on the Virginian governor James Gilmore III. On 1 June 2000, he caved in and ordered new DNA tests using the still relatively new, in the States anyway, technique of short tandem repeats. By 7 September, with no word from the governor's office of what the tests had revealed even though they had the results, Earl Washington's lawyers filed for a pardon. On 2 October, Governor Gilmore granted Washington an absolute pardon for the murder of Rebecca Lynn Williams. Once again, the test results had shown he could not have committed the crime. It was now fifteen years since Earl Washington's innocence had been established by the original blood tests, fifteen years during which he rotted in prison. But it wasn't over. The State of Virginia was to have the last laugh.

The governor refused to pardon Washington for that original gun theft, for hitting his neighbour with a chair and for shooting his brother in the foot. Despite the fact that, if he had just been sentenced for those crimes, he would have been eligible for parole on 25 January 1989 – which was almost twelve years ago. An appeal for leniency, or even common decency, to the Virginia Parole Board was turned down. He stayed in prison.

On 12 February 2001, Earl Washington finally walked free – having served every minute of his sentence for that drunken fracas seventeen years before and having served sixteen years for a murder he did not commit. Even on the day he walked free from the Grensville Correction Center in Jarratt, Virginia, prison officers kept his lawyers and well-wishers away from him and spiritied him off to a supervised flat. 'All I ever wanted from this case was to greet Mr Washington at the prison door,' said Eric M Freedman, the lawyer who had stopped his death sentence all those years before.

By the time Earl Washington left prison, the world had moved on and the impact of his release, while still front-page news, was no longer sensational. The reason for that turn of events was that death-row exonerations were now almost commonplace in the United States. A country, which had plunged back into the business of state sanctioned killing in 1976, was now up to its oxters in wrongful convictions and civil law suits as dead cert killer after dead cert killer walked free as a result of DNA testing. The knock-on effect of all this publicity was to expose the appalling miscarriages of justice, that were taking place within the American legal system, and the widespread corruption engendered by a legal system where prosecutors and police were political appointees desperate for results.

At the forefront of all this uproar has been the Innocence Project. By March 2003, 125 people had been exonerated by the organisation. Many of them would otherwise be dead. All the cases are handled by students at the law school supervised by staff and lawers. There are literally thousands of applications submitted to the project every year. Only those with the best chances of success are taken on. However, the project has transformed DNA testing into a major factor in changing the criminal justice system. It has provided scientific proof that legal systems convict and sentence innocent people – and that wrongful convictions are not isolated or rare events. It has become a powerful echo of that first ever DNA case, in which a young man walked free, thanks to the work of Sir Alec Jeffreys.

There is now a national organisation, called the Innocence Network, whose remit is to set up and support Innocence Projects, similar to the one in New York, across the United States.

Not all exonerations in the US have taken place as a result of the Innocence Project nor have all of them come about through DNA evidence. But, at the time of writing, 102 people, who would not otherwise have been exonerated, have been rescued from Death Row. The vast bulk of these exonerations has taken place during the last decade when DNA testing has matured into a reliable and stable forensic tool. But there are still around 3,600 people on Death Row in the United States where forty states have the death sentence. And George W Bush's old state of Texas still leads the way in the number of executions, followed by Virginia. By October, 802 people had been executed in the twenty-six years since the penalty was brought back into use in the United States. How many of them were innocent?

There are signs the tide is turning and the role of the Innocence Project in this cannot be overestimated. The killings peaked in 1999, when the Texas death factory was in full flow, with ninety-eight executions. But, since then, the figures have started to slide as death-row opponents have begun to make real inroads by highlighting the appalling number of false convictions. In 2000, eighty-five people were put to death. The following year the number fell again to sixty-six and, in 2002, it was down to fifty-three. There are other serious issues. Apart from wrongful convictions, the American Civil Liberty Union points out the fact that 176 black people have been executed for killing white people in the United States but only twelve white people have been executed for killing black people.

By the end of 2001, sixty-two local authorities in the United States had called for a moratorium on the death penalty. A number of states had complied but none as spectacularly as Illinois where the pro-execution governor, George Ryan, suspended the executions of more than 100 prisoners while he set up an investigation to examine the flaws in the system. In January 2003, as he stepped down from office, he pardoned four men and commuted the sentences of a further 167 to life. However, not everybody is convinced that the legal system is so flawed that few executions are sound. The United States Government carried out the first state execution in 2001 around the same time as New Mexico carried out its first modern execution. In Maryland, where a moratorium had been imposed, Robert L Erlich was elected governor on the basis that he would begin executions on taking office in January 2003. The moratorium was duly lifted and the machinery of death was put back in place. At the time of writing, seven people are scheduled to die.

11

BLAKE

All that remains of Roger Keith Coleman's thirty-one short years on
Earth sits inside a freezer deep in the bowels of a building on Research
Drive, Richmond, California. It's not much to show for a life. Just a few
molecules of DNA material, extracted from his body more than a
decade ago, then popped into a phial and placed under carefully
maintained refrigeration. It's not even Roger Keith Coleman's original
DNA. It's a copy created by the PCR process. But this particular DNA
contains much more than a genetic code. It contains the answer to
whether the United States has ever executed an innocent person. Despite
the growing numbers of death-row exonerations and the proliferation
of miscarriages of justice, the United States has yet to wake up to the
cold, hard proof that the state has killed an innocent person. Roger
Keith Coleman may be that proof. It would be a devastating indictment
of the death penalty. For that reason, the microscopic fragments of his
remains have become the battleground for one of the most extraordinary
fights in legal history.

On 20 May 1992, as Coleman was strapped into the electric chair in
Virginia, he was asked if he had anything to say. He did. 'An innocent
man is going to be murdered tonight. When my innocence is proven,
I hope Americans will realize the injustice of the death penalty as all
other civilized countries have.' Bold words, brave words but, ultimately,
when the switch was thrown, they seemed destined to become just
more words of innocence from a convicted murderer who couldn't face
up to the enormity of his crime.

And Coleman was no saint. Of that there was little doubt. On the
evening of 10 March 1983 – the evening that led him to the electric
chair – he had just reached the tender age of twenty-two. As he drove
to work at a mine deep in Appalachians, he already had more than a
whiff of trouble about him. Most people vaguely knew he had a

183

conviction for attempted rape. But he was going straight and, as he rolled up to the mine in his truck for the 10.30 p.m. shift, he was just another small-town wild boy. When he arrived, he got the news that the shift was cancelled. He hung about for a while, talking to an old high school friend, then he got into his truck and headed back down the mountain to the town of Grundy. And that is the end of the known facts about that particular evening – as far as they pertain to Roger Keith Coleman, anyway.

Not far away, Roger Coleman's sister-in-law, Wanda McCoy, was at home alone in her little house by the river waiting for her husband, Brad, to return from work, as usual, at 11 p.m. But, when he walked in the door, she wasn't there to greet him. She was lying dead in the bedroom with her throat cut. She had been brutally raped. In the hullabaloo that followed, everybody remembered Roger Coleman's attempted rape conviction four years ago. A pubic hair was taken from the bedroom and a blood sample. The sample was tested and revealed that Coleman was in the 13 per cent of the population that had that blood type. Of course, there was other evidence – Wanda McCoy's door had not been forced and it was said that Coleman was one of only three people she would have let in the house. And, when he was arrested, the bottoms of his jeans were damp, suggesting that he could have waded through the creek to get to the house unseen. Oh, and, luckily, a jailhouse snitch testified that Coleman had confessed in prison. On those circumstantial stands of evidence alone, he was convicted and sentenced to death.

Years later, in 1990 Coleman, awaiting execution, had become something of a cause célèbre. *Time Magazine* had featured him on the cover under the heading 'Is an innocent man going to die?'. His blood had been taken again – this time by his own lawyers. It was sent to the laboratory of a research scientist named Dr Edward Blake for examination using the newish science of forensic DNA testing. Although he hadn't quite reached celebrity status yet, Dr Blake was on the road to becoming one of the most famous DNA scientists of them all. He often worked with Scheck and Neufeld and his speciality was taking the testing of DNA samples to the limit. Dr Blake was – and is – a perfectionist. His laboratory could squeeze the very last drop of information form the most reluctant, degraded piece of DNA material.

He was in big demand by defence teams and feared by prosecutors. It was said that, after Edward Blake had tested a sample and found a different result from prosecutors, nobody – but nobody – would retest. The man was that good.

The tests he did on Roger Keith Coleman were not retested. Not because they exonerated him – because they didn't. The results were inconclusive. And, if anything, they slightly reduced the likelihood that Coleman was an innocent man. But this was 1990 and DNA testing was in its infancy. Coleman's samples had been subjected to the DQ Alpha process which, as everyone knew, wasn't really very accurate at all. And there was a rumour that there were faint signs that two people had been involved. However, they were too faint. It had been Coleman's last throw of the dice. He was executed before any better system of DNA testing came along.

And so the matter should have rested. Except Roger Keith Coleman wasn't forgotten. A charity, called the Centurion Ministries, which investigates wrongful convictions, had taken up his case. They discovered that Wanda McCoy's door might have been forced open after all. There was a jemmy mark on the inside of it. A woman signed an affidavit saying that she had heard two local men boasting that they had raped and killed Wanda. A member of the jailhouse snitch's family revealed that that damming testimony had been made up. Pressure started to grow to for a re-examination of the Coleman case. As the years wore on and the startling advances in DNA fingerprinting became widely known, it was obvious that new tests could produce new results. And, these new results could settle the issue once and for all. Those DNA samples sitting in Dr Blake's laboratory were going to come in useful.

Then an extraordinary thing happened. The Virginia State authorities demanded that Dr Blake return the Roger Keith Coleman sample. Was the state about to end a murder mystery which had puzzled people for years? Was Coleman about to be posthumously exonerated? Absolutely not. The State of Virginia wanted Roger Keith Coleman's samples returned so they could destroy them in order to prevent any new testing. This was what they had done in other execution cases. Once again the United States was proving the lie that it is the world leader in human rights.

Still, for all its apparent faults, the United States can boast of one startling difference from Britain – openness. In Britain, where it is normal for public bodies and even medium-sized companies to surround themselves with batteries of press and public relations officers, it is almost impossible to gain direct access to senior figures. Calls or e-mails go into a system designed to obscure, cloud and control the flow of information. Interviews are rationed, statements are pruned, personnel are shielded. To contact senior figures in the Forensic Science Service, for example, it is difficult, slow and rarely possible to speak to them face to face. Imagine then, how surprising it is for someone used to such procedures to pick up the phone, dial the number of a company called Forensic Science Associates in California and be put straight through to the most famous DNA scientist in the country. That's what I did one afternoon late in 2002. There were no secretaries in between, no subtle rerouting of the call to a public relations department, no insistence that the request be put in writing. Instead, Dr Blake picks up the phone and begins to talk. What he says should gladden hearts around the world.

'Will I return the sample?' he asks. 'No. It is mine. It is a copy of the original and I have maintained it for all these years. Barry Scheck has told me that I don't really have a case but my view is that the state is wrong. It is a fundamental violation of everything a democracy stands for to destroy evidence. The State of Virginia does not want the testing done because they fear that they would be seen as the first court to have approved the execution of an innocent man. The fact that this kind of ruling came from Virginia, where our founding fathers came from, is simply shameful.'

'And why,' I say, 'do you not then retest the sample lying in your freezer? Solve the mystery once and for all?'

'It is a question of honour,' he says. 'It will not be retested without the approval of a court. Coleman's sister is still alive. She could try and have it done as the executor of his estate. But I won't retest.'

And so Roger Keith Coleman's sample still lies in that fridge. In November 2002, four newspapers and the Centurion Ministries joined forces in a second attempt to have the sample brought back home. They petitioned the Virginia Supreme Court to have it retested. They were refused. 'We have no difficulty concluding that permitting testing

186

of this type would not play a significant positive role in the functioning of the judicial process,' the judges pronounced. In plain speak, it means simply that Roger Keith Coleman is dead and whether he is an innocent man or not is nowhere near as important as upholding the myth that the law is never wrong. Blake shakes his head at such pronouncements. A veteran now of dozens of high profile DNA cases, he believes the judicial system they have exposed is not far short of scandalous.

'It is shameful, the situation that exists here in the United States. As far as individual liberty is concerned, it is dead in the US.'

If you visit the web site of Blake's company in California, he has a link that will take you to a Canadian case where DNA evidence overturned a wrongful conviction. He suggests every American law student should read it. The reason? The Canadians, like the British and Australians, have set up independent commissions to investigate how such miscarriages of justice could have taken place. It's called learning from your mistakes, making sure they do not happen again, being open and accountable. Consider what the British government did in the Hanratty case.

It is a stark contrast with the position in Virginia. But Virginia is not alone. Despite more than 100 exonerations in the United States on the basis of DNA evidence, not a single enquiry has been carried out, anywhere in the country, into the reasons that those miscarriages of justice took place.

Blake continues, 'Every US ambassador should have that thrown back in their faces. DNA has proven the states made mistakes. There isn't room for debate on that. We have convicted people falsely beyond reasonable doubt and we're not asking how that happened. The only way you can do that, with a few exceptions, is if you frame somebody.' And that is the missing link in the growth of DNA exonerations in the United States. The question that is never legally asked and, therefore, never answered is: 'How many of the innocent people, who found themselves in prison, were not just victims of errors or bad lawyering but were actually framed?' If Roger Keith Coleman – or any other person executed for murder – ever turns out to have been innocent, it will be a hard question to avoid answering. And, when that happens, a whole legal system will have to change – thanks to the discovery made in a laboratory in Leicestershire almost twenty years ago.

The changes that have taken place to forensic DNA fingerprinting since Alec Jeffreys had his Eureka moment have been startling. The technique has gone through many different revisions and a not a few setbacks to reach levels of accuracy and sophistication that are quite amazing. The science has grown up and matured and become utterly commonplace. In Britain, where the march of the National DNA Database continues at an astounding pace, new revisions of the law will ensure that every person arrested will be swabbed and sampled and have their DNA profile entered into the computer database in Birmingham. Now, DNA testing is fast, reliable, extremely accurate and, most of all, cheap.

To illustrate how much it has become an everyday tool, let us consider one last story. It is not very exciting but it is mine. On the evening of 5 November 2002, my family car was broken into as it sat on the drive of my home in Glasgow. The radio cassette player was stolen. It was the lowest of crimes, opportunistic, extremely common and almost victimless. The insurance company would replace the radio cassette. It would probably be sold for around £20 or swapped for drugs. It would certainly never be seen again by me.

By 11 a.m. the next morning, as two scene of crime officers rang the doorbell, a replacement was already being sought. They looked over the car and then brought out two swabs the size of cotton buds and proceeded to wipe along the door handles and inside the vehicle. Within minutes, they were in my kitchen dipping the swabs into test tubes containing clear liquid. What were they doing? DNA testing the car. Trying to pick up traces of sweat or grease from fingerprints that would yield a profile to compare on the National Database. For a two-bob crime. Today, saliva on the inside of a balaclava, dandruff, moisture on discarded food – all these things can now be swabbed to extract the most minute pieces of DNA material. And that is all the scientists need to produce a result under the latest SGM Plus system. As the officers went back outside, they asked me if I smoked. They then began to scour the drive for cigarette butts that the thieves might have thrown away – these could be DNA tested.

Purely by coincidence, I knew exactly where these samples were going because I had visited their final destination only days before. I had driven that same car into the centre of town and manoeuvred it into a space in the incredibly tight underground car park beneath Pitt Street Police Station, the headquarters of Strathclyde Police. Then I had taken the lift and not a few stairs and walked into a wide pale-coloured corridor, which is off-limits to police officers. There, Martin Fairley, the youthful head of Strathclyde Police Forensic Division, had met me and shown me exactly how commonplace, yet sophisticated, DNA testing had become.

In a room off a side corridor, two machines, the size of mini fridges, stood on tables. They looked like photocopiers. This equipment was all that was needed to test samples using the SGM Plus system. White-coated staff worked nearby checking the results and making sure they were fed down the line to the National Database in Birmingham. It was all pretty ordinary. Pretty everyday. As DNA testing has become.

In the near future, samples won't even need to go to labs. Scene of crime officers will be able to test them on the spot using portable units. Work is taking place to use DNA markers that will identify specific human physical characteristics – and a person's race can already be identified. In a recent interview, the head of the Birmingham DNA Unit predicted that hair colour, face shape and other defining features would, one day, be among the details that the testing machines can identify.

Later that day, while sitting in the office of a senior police officer, I was told two interesting facts. The first was that DNA testing was now so commonplace that ordinary fingerprinting will become redundant sooner rather than later. The second was that senior police officers all over the world are complaining of a new problem afflicting their men – DNA-itis. It boils down to the simple fact that police officers have become so reliant on DNA evidence that, if they can't find any, they think the case is lost. Expect a drive to bring back old-fashioned policing methods.

Wherever you look, there is no denying the consequences of Alec Jeffreys discovery. So, what of the man who set it all in motion? Where is Alec Jeffreys. Well, he is now Professor Sir Alec Jeffreys but he is not sitting at the top of some fat American corporation making millions from the seeds of his success – although he has had the offers. He is still, at the time of writing, in the same laboratory in Leicestershire, sitting at the same desk. His title may have changed in recognition of what he has achieved but he hasn't.

'And how do you feel looking at what has sprung from this well?' I ask. 'Amazed and proud,' he says. Has he become rich on the proceeds? He laughs. 'You're not looking at an enormously wealthy man.' He points to an aerial photograph stuck to the wall. It is beside the one with the heading 'World's First DNA Fingerprint'. It shows a small cottage in Cornwall. 'We managed to buy that with my royalties,' he says. 'So we have done all right out of it.'

So have quite a few other people.

POSTSCRIPT

Few people are entirely ready to go to their grave but, in 1990, as forty-nine-year-old Joe Kappen lay on his death bed, racked with cancer, he may have consoled himself with the knowledge that, in death, he would finally evade justice for the brutal slayings of three teenage girls in Wales in 1973. Police had never stopped hunting for the murderer of teenagers Pauline Floyd and Geraldine Hughes whose deaths became known as the Babes in the Wood case. They also suspected that these killings were linked to the murder of Sandra Newton whose body had been discovered at nearby Briton Ferry three months earlier. But detectives were nowhere near catching Kappen when he passed away, taking with him the secrets of the Llandarcy killings – or so it seemed.

For twelve years, the body of pub bouncer Kappen lay a-mouldering in the grave but then police scientists stumbled upon a technique which would be used to track him down through his family. It would prove too late for Kappen to be punished for his crimes but South Wales Police ensured his guilt was well publicised and, in the process, they drew attention to the method they had used to identify him. Ears of police forces all over the country were pricking up as detectives scrutinised old cases to see if any of them were suitable for undergoing DNA familial testing, as the new system was to be known.

By the summer of 2003, the technique had been substantially refined and was being hailed as a major scientific breakthrough that would be the next big thing in DNA fingerprinting. The next big thing it may well turn out to be but a significant scientific breakthrough it was not. In fact, in a testament to the adage that history repeats itself, the new system was really just the same as the method used by Alec Jeffreys in the first ever DNA fingerprinting case, all those years ago, but with some refinements. Could it be put to use in the search for the perpetrators of other unsolved murders? Would it, for example, be of

191

use in what the press, in 1977, had dubbed 'The World's End Murders'?

In Edinburgh, on the night of 15 October 1977, two seventeen-year-old girls, Helen Scott and Christine Eadie, headed out for a night on the town. They met two other girlfriends, visited a few bars and ended up in the World's End Pub on the Royal Mile – it had been so named because, in the sixteenth century, it was located outside the city walls and was, to the good burghers of Edinburgh, literally at the end of their world. The pub was heaving and Helen and Christine sat down at a table opposite the door where they were soon deep in conversation with two men. At some point, their friends came over and suggested they all went on to a party but the girls decided to stay where they were and continue chatting. That was the last time they were definitely seen alive. The next day their names would become entwined forever with the name of the pub.

What happened to them? Well, they may have been seen later by a couple walking up the High Street later that night. They recalled passing two girls with two men. One of the girls seemed to have had a few drinks and she slipped out of her shoe as she walked. At this point, she was heard to call out 'Chris' to her friend. However, nobody could definitely say it was Helen and Christine they'd seen.

The girls' bodies were found the next morning. Both teenagers, on the cusp of life, had been brutally beaten, raped and strangled. Christine was discovered, naked, by a couple out walking on the foreshore at Gosford Beach fourteen miles from Edinburgh. Helen's partially clothed body was discovered just a few miles away in a corn stubble field. The murders sent shock waves throughout the country and beyond.

Back in 1977, police did not have the forensic means available to them to make much of the samples taken from the bodies. But that did not dilute the scale of the enquiry. At the time, it was the biggest ever carried out in Scotland with more than 1,300 people being interviewed. Sadly, it came to nothing. The girls lived on in the memories of their families, in the pages of Scottish crime books and in the files held by detectives at Lothian and Borders Police Force but nobody was caught or even charged.

Then a now familiar scenario began to unfold. The samples, that had been taken from the bodies of Helen Scott and Christine Eadie and which the police had held for all those years, were sent for forensic testing. There was a new technique called Low Copy Number (LCN) DNA profiling and its advantage was its ability to amplify the most unpromising, degraded, tiny samples into usable DNA profiles. After all this time, it would be a gamble but, as it turned out, it was one that paid off. When the results came back they dramatically revealed that the same DNA profile had been obtained from the samples taken from each of the girls – which meant that the police could, with a huge degree of certainty, assume that the same man was involved in both rapes and murders. Having got this information, it was now surely just a matter of loading the DNA profile into the National DNA Database and hoping for a match. A nation held its breath but there was no match. Whoever had left that evidence at the murder scenes had never been DNA tested – ever. For the police and others involved, it was desperately frustrating. They knew that the killer was out there and, with his incriminating evidence on file, all they had to do was find him. But how could they get to him?

And that was the way things were when Lothian and Borders Police became aware of the Kappen case and learned of the system the police in Wales had used to track him down. Traces of Kappen's DNA had been left when he murdered the girls but, because he too had never been DNA tested, the police had no way of linking the DNA to the guilty man.

However, DNA profiling had been used to prove the parentage of children so could it work the other way round? Could the DNA of a person's child lead forensic scientists to that person? The verdict was that it could. The only question now was whether any of the murderer's children had been DNA tested. If not, then they would have hit another brick wall.

Speaking of the Kappen case, Bob Bramley of the Forensic Science Service revealed that 'scientists decided to use the fact that DNA patterns between family members, although by no means identical, can be strikingly similar. So, working on the assumption that criminality also runs in families, it was suggested we look for similar matches on the database. Sure enough it came up with a son of one of the known suspects from the time.' The man whose name matched that record was interviewed, his family were traced and police were led to the graveyard containing Kappen's body. It was dug up and samples were taken away for DNA testing. There was a complete match and police knew, without any doubt, that Kappen was their man.

Could this also work in the World's End cases? When the DNA samples taken from Christine and Helen were run through the National DNA Database, there were 200 partial hits. That meant that, even though the murderer himself was not on file, there were 200 men – for they were all men – who could be related to the person who had killed the two girls. This technique may not have been new but this was genetic sleuthing on an entirely different scale.

In September 2003, Lothian and Borders Police announced they were about to begin the lengthy process of interviewing every person whose name had been turned up by the database. Detective Inspector Alan Jones said priority would be given to any of those who appeared to have a link with the immediate area. If this failed to produce a conclusion, they would spread their net to the rest of Scotland and beyond. Speaking to the Scottish press, DI Jones said he hoped the investigation would resolve the case and provide some closure for the relatives and friends of the murdered girls. He added, 'We're not taking anything for granted but we are hopeful because other major investigations have succeeded, after many years, using this technology. Many offenders come from families with a background of criminality and we might just be able to link into the genetic seam that we are looking for.'

At the time of writing, the hunt for the World's End murderer or murderers continues. Doors are being knocked on and huge numbers of police man-hours are being logged. If this enormous effort eventually leads to an arrest, we can be sure the practice of checking the database for partial hits will become far more commonplace and it could provide one way of bypassing the problems that arise when criminals have managed to avoid ever being DNA tested. There are currently 200,000 unmatched crime scene samples on the National DNA Database. It galls the authorities that the criminals those samples belong to are still out there – at large.

Of course, DNA familial testing is just an updated variation of the technique Alec Jeffreys had used to establish that the schoolboy Andrew Sarbah was a British citizen and not, as the Home Office had insisted, an illegal immigrant. Two decades have passed since the Sarbah case, the historic first one ever to use DNA fingerprinting, and the fact that the technique had been improved and honed merely shows how settled this science has become. Whether the police and the Forensic Science Service are still chipping away at new frontiers in DNA testing or merely rediscovering old ones are side issues really – what matters is that Alec Jeffreys' discovery continues to have a breathtaking impact on the modern world. The science works beautifully and the next stage of the DNA revolution – getting as many people as possible on to national DNA databases – is taking place.

Britain has always led the way in ensuring that its national database would be fully backed by laws that will allow it to be as all encompassing as possible. Like Topsy it has just grown and grown. In the middle of 2003, the UK government announced that the number of records contained in the National DNA Database had passed the two million mark, with scientists processing around 3,000 samples a day. It is now being predicted that, within five years, the time taken to turn DNA material into a DNA profile will be reduced from a couple of days to a couple of minutes. It has also been forecast that the number of cells needed to create a full profile will drop from a couple of hundred to just one or two. So it's no wonder that lawyers in the United States routinely advise their clients not to smoke, drink from a cup or spit when in police custody.

The British government has revealed that the sophisticated hand-held DNA testers, that police will one day carry, are to have integral radio devices which will allow them to check instantly with the National DNA Database. It is entirely possible, officials predict, that officers will leave the scene of a crime knowing the name and address of the person who committed it. Even in cases where a person's DNA has not been entered on the National DNA Database, more sophisticated profiling techniques will enable officers to work out the eye and hair colour of the suspect – and all of this will be done without officers even having to return to the police station. It is little wonder that many commentators acidly observed that the announcement of these details coincided with the one hundredth anniversary of the birth of George Orwell, the author of *1984* and the creator of Big Brother.

In September of 2003, it seemed that nothing would be allowed to get in the way of this headlong rush into the brave new world of law enforcement. Home Secretary David Blunkett announced that he wanted the double jeopardy rule – one of the fundamental tenets of British law and a principle that has been adopted by every other civilised country in the world – abolished. Double jeopardy is one of those legal rules that has fascinated authors for centuries. Basically, it ensures that, once a person has been tried and acquitted of a crime, he or she cannot be tried for the same crime again. It seems to exist only to prevent a retrial on the introduction of new evidence. And it is that point which has formed the central thrust of so many books and films. However, that masks the real reason for the existence of the double jeopardy rule – its main purpose is to protect the public from a potentially malicious state. Without it, suspects could be continually retried and retried until a conviction has been obtained.

Mr Blunkett's argument that it was time to dump double jeopardy was based on the simple fact that, in many old cases, DNA profiling was now providing irrefutable new evidence. Why should a murderer or rapist be allowed to stay free just because the technology to convict him or her had not been available at the original trial? It is a powerful point but it was not powerful enough to convince the House of Lords. They rejected the proposal on the grounds that it would place too much power in the hands of the prosecuting authorities. That is not the end of the story though. The issue will return, the government will try to have the law changed again and they will probably succeed. Once more the consequences of Alec Jeffreys' discovery will be changing the world. Whether that will be for better or for worse, only time will tell.

Perhaps unsurprisingly nobody seemed particularly troubled by the possible abandonment of the double jeopardy rule. Maybe the public have become so accepting of the wonders of DNA profiling that they have no qualms whatsoever about its safety. Certainly, far more excitement seemed to be generated, in the autumn of 2003, by the revelation that 75 per cent of the DNA of poodles is exactly the same as that of humans. Considering that more than 99 per cent of the genetic make-up of all human beings is identical, this probably shouldn't have come as that much of a surprise.

It was that point, or a slight variation of it, which prompted Professor James Watson, who along with Francis Crick had discovered the existence of the DNA double helix, to step out of his laboratory and issue a warning that their discovery, if not used carefully, still had as much power to harm individuals as it had to do good. The year 2003 was the fiftieth anniversary of Watson and Crick's discovery. Watson, the younger of the duo, is now seventy-five and still working as a leading scientists in the USA. With interest aroused by the anniversary, he called for a worldwide DNA database containing everybody's details. It could, the professor said, be a vital weapon in the fight against terrorism. In the wake of the September 11 attacks, few would argue with him. He told the *Independent* newspaper:

It is not that I am insensitive to the concerns about individual privacy or to the potential for inappropriate use of genetic information but it [the proposed worldwide DNA database] would make life safer. The sacrifice of this particular form of anonymity does not seem an unreasonable price to pay, provided the laws see to a strict and judicious control over access to public data . . . It would be harder to be a crook . . . If you want to make the criminal justice system more fair, what's wrong with it?

It's hard to imagine that, in 100 years from now, we won't have it . . . With the increase in terrorism, we want to know who people are.

It fell, once again, to Sir Alec Jeffreys to point out that DNA profiling, although a wonderful science, still had its limitations. In particular, he said, the way all modern DNA techniques amplify tiny fragments of DNA, turning snapshots of it into full profiles, was potentially risky. 'In theory, you can narrow it down to a single cell and that can come from almost anything – hair, nail clippings,' he said. 'But you can get into dangerous territory with this because you don't know where it's come from if it's such a small sample. We're all potentially covered in bits of other people.'

Separating out where DNA samples have come from will be the next big challenge for the science. If it is not dealt with properly, it could destroy all the gains that have already been made. It's a threat that the criminal fraternity has already cottoned on to. In the United States, a convicted rapist, Anthony Turner, was almost freed from prison after his DNA turned up at a rape he couldn't have committed because he was in prison at the time it happened. Turner claimed it was a mismatch and that somebody else shared the same DNA as him despite the astronomical odds. The case set alarm bells ringing throughout the DNA community. Had a mistake really been made? It turned out Turner had had his semen smuggled out of prison in a ketchup packet and a member of his family had paid a woman to stage a phony rape. He was sentenced to 120 years in prison for the scam.

However, few people involved in the case missed the warning that, if the manipulation of DNA evidence were to become widespread, the whole system could collapse. 'The scary part was here was this really bad guy who understood the science [and] was trying to use it to defeat us,' Milwaukee prosecutor Norman Gahn said. 'We're going to see more of that as time goes on.'

BIBLIOGRAPHY

In the writing of this book, the author consulted the following publications. They appear in chapter relevancy order.

Pena, S D J, Chakraborty, R and Epplen, J T, Jeffreys, A J (eds), *DNA Fingerprinting: State of the Science* (Birkhauser: Verlag AG: 1993)

Fridell, Ron, *DNA Fingerprinting: the Ultimate Identity*, (Franklin Watts: 2001)

Coleman, Howard and Swenson, Eric (eds), *DNA in the Courtroom: a Trial Watcher's Guide*, (Genelex Corp: 1995)

Dunne, Dominick, *Justice: Crimes, Trials, and Punishments*, (Time Warner Paperbacks: 2002)

The Times, 'Gene print frees death case youth': 22 November 1986

The Guardian, 'Youth cleared of girl's murder': 22November 1986

Leicester Mercury, 'Psycho Killer': 15 March 2003

CBS Evening News, 4 May 1995 (transcript)

Press Association, 'Mother attacks film': 16 September 1989

The Guardian, 'Evasive double killer sentenced to life in gaol: how genetic testing caught a murderer': 23 January 1988

The Times, 'Life for sex killer who sent decoy to take genetic test': 23 January 1988

Associated Press, 'Man confesses to murder after DNA fingerprinting leads to arrest': 22 January 1988

The Times, 'Man held over two murders': 22 September 1987

The Times, 'One in 4,000 refuses murder test': 29 July 1987

United Press International, 'Police using genetics to track criminals': 27 March 1987

Los Angeles Times, 'Genetic fingerprints may catch killer': 11 March 1987

Chemical Week, 'The case of a confusing license': 21 January 1987

The Guardian, 'Police in licence row over gene test' and 'Home Office to negotiate with ICI over genetic fingerprinting': 5 January 1987

The Times, 'Genetic fingerprinting row hits hunt for killer': 5 January 1987

The Guardian, 'Killer hunt blood tests' and 'Leicestershire police to use genetic fingerprinting system': 2 January 1987

Financial Times, 'How the genetic trail leads to who did it': 11 December 1987

Press Association, 'Police chief admits blunder over murder book': 21 June 1990

The Independent, 'Invisible print of a killer: Joseph Wambaugh discusses death with Robert Winder': 22 February 1989

The Associated Press, 'Author's book on British slayings rankles police': 17 February 1989

The Washington Post, 'Double Helix, Double Murder': 19 March 1989

Joseph Wambaugh, *The Blooding* (Bantam Books: 1989)[1]

The Guardian, 'Publican on murder charge': 16 February 1988

The Times, 'Publican denies killing woman: Ian Simms': 22 February 1989

The Times, 'Murder jury told of mother's hunt: Helen McCourt': 23 February 1989

The Times, 'Blood trapped man jailed for murder without body': 15 March 1989

The Independent, 'Technique opens avenues for police': 9 January 1993

The Independent, 'Burden of proof: no body, no witness, no motive': 28 January 1995

The Times, 'Judge backs prisoners over interviews with media': 20 December 1996

Mullis, Kary, *Dancing Naked in the Mind Field* (Bloomsbury: 2000)

The Guardian, 'The maverick': 19 April 1999

San Jose Mercury News, 'Nobel laureate Kary Mullis blazes a freewheeling path': 9 March 1999

The Independent, 'British scientists end the long search for Josef Mengele' 5 April 1992

The Independent, 'Anatomy of a murder: Steve Connor on the new scientific techniques that helped police uncover the trail of Karen Price's killer': 7 April 1991

The Observer, 'Fleshing out the bones of murder': 24 April 1994

---

[1] The only written source for the details elicited in police interviews carried out during the Enderby murders inquiry is Joseph Wambaugh's book, *The Blooding*. There was considerable controversy after publication of the book over how Mr Wambaugh managed to get access to these documents. In subsequent years, a number of police officers were disciplined over the issue. During the course of this book, I spoke to a number of people who were involved with the cases at the time. Off the record, they confirmed many of the detailed points.

BIBLIOGRAPHY

The Independent, 'Chance find of skeleton led to "pimp" murder trial': 22 January 1991

Press Association, 'Two charged with "Body in Carpet" murder': 26 February 1990

The Associated Press, 'Appeal set for nation's first DNA-convicted serial killer': 6 June 1989

Los Angeles Times, 'DNA-based conviction upheld in murder case': 23 September 1989

Associated Press, 'Judge refuses to stay execution in DNA conviction': 26 April 1994

Richmond Afro-American, 'Execution appears imminent': 27 April 1994

The Associated Press, 'Serial killer convicted by DNA evidence executed': 27 April 1994

The Virginian-Pilot, 'Execution: southside strangler put to death': 28 April 1994

Deseret News, 'Execution of killer is first based on DNA "hit"': 15 March 2002

Dwyer, Jim Scheck, Barry, Neufeld, Peter, *Actual Innocence* (Signet True Crime: 2001)

The American Lawyer, 'How Barry Scheck and Peter Neufeld tripped up the DNA experts': December 1989

New York Law Journal, 'DNA evidence in criminal cases: legal developments': 25 April 1990

St Louis Post-Dispatch, 'Two cases raise issue of lack of standards in DNA fingerprinting': 20 August 1989

The New York Times, 'Reliability of DNA testing challenged by judge's ruling': 15 August 1989

Newsday, 'Lawyers make DNA test inadmissible': 12 July 1989

The Boston Globe, 'Court use of DNA fingerprinting challenged': 23 May 1989

The Jerusalem Report, 'The unsolved case of "The Angel of Death"': 25 July 1991

The Associated Press, 'Police file charges against four who harbored Mengele': 7 July 1986

Chicago Tribune, 'How Nazi war criminal Josef Mengele cheated justice for 34 years': 18 May 1986

The Associated Press, 'Final forensic report says skeleton was Mengele's': 6 July 1985

Time Magazine, 'Is this the Nazi doctor?': 24 June 1985

Mail on Sunday, 'Hanratty did this to me': 28 April 2002

Hansard, 'House of Commons written answers for 11 June 1997'

Hochmeister, Manfred N, *Use of the GenePrint Multiplex System for The Analysis of DNA in a Serial Killer Case: Profiles in DNA* (Geneprint: 1997)

Corpus Delicti, 'Knowledge solution', Issue 4: June 1997

The Washington Post, 'Vienna's literati championed the convict-turned-writer': 3 August 1994

The Herald, '"Jailhouse poet" accused of killing eleven prostitutes': 21 April, 1994

Los Angeles Times, 'Austrian slayer of LA prostitutes kills self': 30 June 1994

The Scotsman, 'It's all in the genes': 10 July 2001

Press Association, 'Police investigate "Bible John" tip-off': 14 October 2000

Jeffrey, Robert, *Glasgow's Hard Men* (Black & White Publishing: 2002)

The Guardian, 'DNA fingerprinting has been hailed as an infallible aid to solving crime but . . . it is not as reliable as its supporters claim': 15 December 1994

Forensic Science Service: Case Profiles.

Texas Lawyer, 'In session 5th circuit hears arguments in notorious death row cases': 6 May 1996

Chicago Tribune, 'Flawed trials led to death chamber': 11 June 2000

Texas Lawyer, 'Weekly case summaries': 4 December 1995

Lethal Indifference: the Fatal Combination of Incompetent Attorneys and Unaccountable Courts (Texas Defender Service Publication)

Morton, James, *Catching the Killers* (Edbury Press: 2001)

The following people were interviewed by the author: Professor Sir Alec Jeffreys, Chief Superintendent David Baker, Dr Peter Gill and Bob Woffinden, Professor Howard Cooke, Dr James Weber John Quinn, Dr Edward Blake and author's sources at Strathclyde Police.

INDEX